HUDSON'S

Culzean Castle, South West Scotland.

Published by:

Norman Hudson & Company, High Wardington House, Upper Wardington, Banbury, Oxfordshire OX17 1SP

Tel: 01295 750750   Fax: 01295 750800

ISBN: 0 9531426 3 9

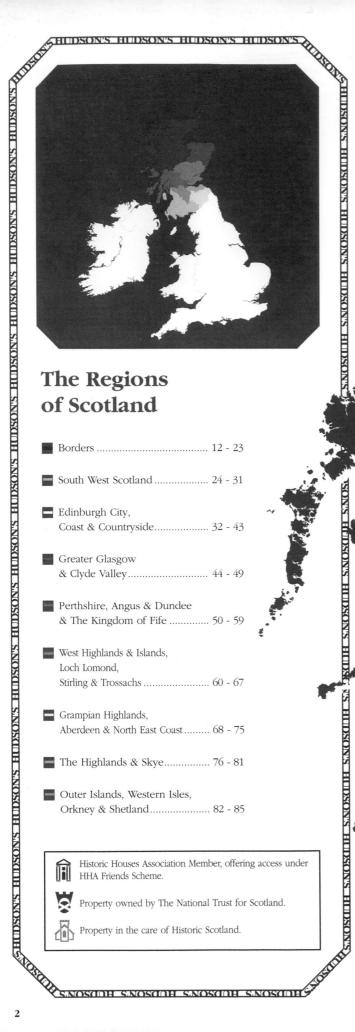

Scotland is divided into nine regions to coincide with Scotland's Area Tourist Boards.

Outer Islands

Outer Islands

Highlands & Skye

Gra

Perthshire/ Fife

West Highlands

Greater Glasgow

Edinburgh

Border

South West

The Regions of Scotland

■ Borders .... 12 - 23

■ South West Scotland .... 24 - 31

■ Edinburgh City,
Coast & Countryside................... 32 - 43

■ Greater Glasgow
& Clyde Valley............................ 44 - 49

■ Perthshire, Angus & Dundee
& The Kingdom of Fife .... 50 - 59

■ West Highlands & Islands,
Loch Lomond,
Stirling & Trossachs .... 60 - 67

■ Grampian Highlands,
Aberdeen & North East Coast .... 68 - 75

■ The Highlands & Skye................ 76 - 81

■ Outer Islands, Western Isles,
Orkney & Shetland...................... 82 - 85

 Historic Houses Association Member, offering access under HHA Friends Scheme.

 Property owned by The National Trust for Scotland.

 Property in the care of Historic Scotland.

The Regions of Scotland

River Coladoir & Ben More, Isle of Mull.   Argyll, The Isles, Loch Lomond, Stirling & Trossachs Tourist Board.

The development of

Scottish Castles

by Martin Coventry

The design of castles depended very much on the social organisation, political climate, expense and building fashions of the time – but it was always a show of the lord's wealth, prestige and power, and a symbol of his authority.

The earliest fortified sites consist of hill forts, brochs and duns, dating from before recorded history. Some of these were occupied as late as the 17th century – and the sites of many others were reused for later fortresses. Hill forts are found all over Scotland, but brochs and duns tend to be concentrated in the north and west.

After the Battle of Hastings, motte and bailey castles were introduced to Scotland along with feudalism – although they are unevenly distributed, being particularly numerous in Galloway, for example, but with few surviving examples in Lothian. This form of defence was not used for long.

By the 13th century, castles of enclosure (enceinte) were being built, where a site was surrounded by a strong stone wall encircling timber or stone buildings. These developed, in some cases, into large castles with large keeps, gatehouses and towers.

Large stone castles were expensive to build and maintain and in the late 14th and 15th centuries simple keeps were built, usually with a small enclosure or courtyard. The keep evolved into the tower house, which was not as massive or simple, and had more regard to comfort. Hundreds of these towers were built in the 16th century. During the later 16th and 17th centuries, the simple rectangular tower house developed into L- and Z-plan tower houses, which provide more accommodation, covering fire and amenity.

At the same time as nobles built and developed keeps and tower houses, the kings of Scots built or refurbished ornate royal palaces. These were often developed out of older strongholds but during the 15th and 16th centuries were remodelled in the Renaissance style to become comfortable residences.

As the need for defence decreased, many castles and tower houses were developed into mansion houses.

There is a great deal of overlap between the different types of stronghold and often a new castle was built on the site of a previous one, and reused materials from the original or simply built around, or out of, the existing building. There are also definite regional differences. In areas such as the Borders, feuds, reiving and warfare

contributed to the building of a large number of simple tower houses, peel towers and bastles, although few of these survive intact; whereas in Grampian there are a large number of 17th century Z-plan tower houses. The topography of particular areas influenced the position and style of building: an island in a marsh was as good a site as a rocky promontory.

Hill forts, Brochs and Duns

Hill forts may date from as early as the Neolithic period to about 500BC, and some were used until medieval times. Ramparts of earth and stone walls, laced with timber, or wooden palisades protected hilltops or other defensible sites. Some hill forts enclosed whole villages within their ramparts.

Brochs and duns date from about 100BC, and a few were occupied into the 17th century.

Mousa Broch.

Brochs are round hollow towers, built of drystone masonry, with very thick walls. These walls were formed from two shells of masonry with a gallery running up inside the wall. The entrance was extremely narrow, allowing only one person at a time to enter, and a small guard chamber defended the entrance. There were often many buildings around the broch, with outer ditches and ramparts to defend the settlement. Brochs appear to have been concentrated in Orkney and Shetland, Caithness and Sutherland, and the Western Isles, but there are also examples in other parts of the country, including Lothian and Dumfries and Galloway.

The best remaining examples of brochs are Mousa and Clickhimin (Shetland), Dun Carloway (Lewis), Midhowe and Gurness (Orkney), Dun Dornigail (Sutherland), the Glen Elg brochs (Lochaber) and Dun Beag (Skye).

Duns are also most thickly concentrated in the north and west. Dun in Gaelic means fortified place and is used for both duns and brochs in Gaelic-speaking areas.

The general distribution of duns is similar to that of brochs but duns are usually irregular in plan, following the contours of a rock, and can vary in size from a small homestead to a hill fort. The building style was very similar to brochs, and they often had galleried walls and small cells within the walls. Dun an Sticar and Dun Ban on North Uist are good examples of duns, although both were occupied into medieval times.

It is hard to see how it has been possible to always distinguish the two types of structures, when existing remains of both are so fragmentary and overbuilt. It is also not clear who they were built to defend against, although it may have been Roman slave ships.

Motte and Bailey Castles
(12th century)

During the 12th century, motte and bailey castles were introduced along with feudalism into Scotland, mostly into lowland areas, where the style was adopted and adapted by native lords. Motte and bailey castles are mostly concentrated in Clydesdale, Galloway and Grampian. There appear to have been few in central Scotland, Lothians, the north-west and the Highlands.

Motte and bailey castles consisted of an earthern mound, known as a motte, and a courtyard, or bailey, enclosed by a wooden palisade and defended by a ditch. The plan of the motte was usually round, but some were also oval or rectangular and used existing defensive features such as ravines, spits of land between rivers, or cliff tops. At the base of the motte was a dry or wet ditch or moat.

A wooden tower was built on the motte, where the lord and his followers could shelter if attacked. The bailey contained many buildings, such as the hall, chapel, kitchen, bakehouse and stables. The

Caerlaverock Castle.

motte and bailey were linked by a removable bridge which spanned the ditch.

Often all that remains today is evidence of the earthworks, some good examples of these being Motte of Urr (Galloway), Peel Ring of Lumphanan and Doune of Invernochty (both Gordon). Duffus Castle (Moray) and Rothesay Castle (Bute) are two of the few examples where a stone keep was added. Other mottes and their surrounding earthworks were reused by later castle builders.

Wooden castles were not used for long, as they could be set alight, but had the advantage of being easy and quick to build. Most of the castles built by Edward I of England to control Scotland were built of wood; after his costly Welsh campaigns, which included the building of such massive castles as Caernarvon, he could afford little else.

Stone Castles of Enclosure or Enceinte *(12/13th century)*

Stone began to be used as a building material because it was less vulnerable to attack by fire and because it was easily obtainable.

Stone castles of enclosure were built as early as the 12th century, but the majority appeared in the 13th century. The simplest form was a wall enclosing a two-storey hall block of wood or stone. The entrance to the hall block was on the first floor and was reached by a ladder, which could be removed easily during attack. The wall was usually surrounded by a ditch and rampart.

There are some good examples of castles of enclosure on the western side of Scotland, including Castle Sween (Argyll), Castle Tioram (Morvern) and Mingary Castle (Ardnamurchan).

By the 13th century, walls were heightened and strengthened, enclosing a courtyard which contained both the hall and lord's chamber, as well as kitchens, bakeries, brewhouses, stables and storerooms. Corner towers were added to defend the castle. The walls were pierced by slits through which crossbows could be fired.

The weakest part of these castles was the entrance through the wall and strong gatehouses were added with portcullises, drawbridges, iron-studded doors and murder-holes. The curtain walls were given battlements for archers to shelter behind.

By the 14th century, large stone castles such as Bothwell Castle (Lanarkshire), Caerlaverock Castle (Dumfries) and Kildrummy Castle (Grampian) had

been built. These castles had a keep – a large strong tower separate from the rest of the castle – as well as a gatehouse. The keep had a hall and chambers for the lord. These castles also had thick curtain walls with round or square corner towers.

There are relatively few large castles left in Scotland, partly due to the expense of constructing and maintaining such large buildings, and partly because many were destroyed by the Scots, during the Wars of Independence, so that they could not be reused by the English. However, some strong royal castles were maintained, including those at Edinburgh, Stirling, Roxburgh, Dumbarton and Dunbar, and a few of the most powerful families could also afford massive fortresses such as the Douglas strongholds of Tantallon (Lothian) and Threave (Galloway) and the Keith stronghold of Dunnottar (Grampian).

Simple Keeps *(14/15th century)*

These consisted of a simple square or rectangular tower, usually with an adjoining courtyard. The walls of the keep were thick and normally rose to at least three storeys to a flush crenellated parapet. The basement and first floor were vaulted to increase the strength of the building. The size of the keep depended on the wealth of the builder.

The basement contained a cellar, often with no connection to the floor above. The hall was on the first floor, with a private chamber for the lord on the floor above, and a garret storey above this. The thick walls contained many mural chambers, either small bedrooms or garderobes. The entrance was at first-floor level and was reached by an external timber stair, which could be removed during an attack. Stairs led up, within the walls, to each floor. The keep was roofed with stone slates, or slabs, to protect the keep against attack by fire.

The courtyard enclosed buildings such as a kitchen, stables, chapel, brewhouse, and was surrounded by a wall often with a ditch and drawbridge.

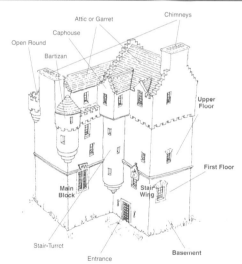

Diagram of L-plan tower house, showing the three main floors:

The basement contained the entrance, at the foot of the stair-wing, and was occupied by a kitchen, wine-cellar and food-cellar. The main turnpike stair only climbed to the first-floor hall, while the upper floors were reached by a turnpike stair in the turret in the re-entrant angle. The lord's private chamber was on the floor above the hall, although there was little privacy for the rest of the household, as each room opened from the last. The turret stair rose up to the parapet and was crowned by a caphouse and watch-chamber.

The tower would have had a walled courtyard, or barmkin, enclosing ranges of buildings, including stabling, workshops, a brewhouse and more accommodation.

The walls of the tower were usually harled and whitewashed. The heraldic panel showed the arms of the lord and his wife, who used her own family name, and the date of building or alteration.

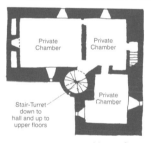

Upper floor.

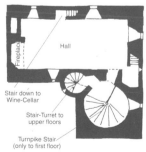

First floor.

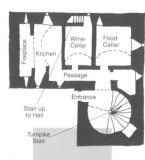

Basement.

Royal Palaces *(15/16th century)*

The Stewart kings spent much of their energy acquiring wealth, usually by forfeiting unpopular subjects. They built or remodelled royal palaces in the Renaissance style at Stirling, Holyrood (Edinburgh), Linlithgow (West Lothian) and Falkland (Fife).

Tower Houses *(16th century)*

In 1535 an Act of Parliament declared that every landed man that had land valued at £100 (Scots) was to build a tower or castle to defend his lands.

Although there is no clear divide, tower houses evolved from keeps. The walls became less thick and the entrance was moved to the basement. Parapets were corbelled-out so that they would overhang the wall and missiles could be dropped on attackers below. The corners had open rounds and the stair was crowned by a caphouse and watch-chamber. Gunloops and shot-holes replaced arrowslits. The walls were harled and often whitewashed.

Tower houses also underwent change and adaption in the 16th century. After the Reformation, with the increased wealth of Protestant landowners and the increased availability of land, which had previously belonged to the Church, many examples of more comfortable tower houses were built. These were mostly in the north-east, the central belt and the south, including the Borders and Galloway.

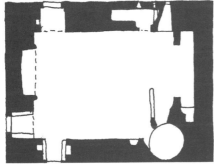

Plan of 16th century tower house.

The reduction in need for defensive features meant that these later tower houses were more spacious and comfortable. The structures were still built vertically and most continued to have one room on each floor. However, wings or towers were either incorporated into or added to the design. Good examples of tower houses can be found at Smailholm Tower (Borders), Crathes Castle (Grampian) and Amisfield Tower (Dumfries & Galloway).

L-plan Tower Houses

(mid-16th century)

The L-plan tower house had a stair-wing added to the main block. The stair was usually turnpike and climbed only to the hall on the first floor. The upper floors were reached by a turnpike stair in a small stair-turret corbelled out, above first-floor level, in the re-entrant angle. This stair was crowned by a caphouse and watch-chamber. In some cases, the wing contained a stair which climbed to all floors and

Plan of 16th century L-plan tower house.

sometimes a separate stair-tower stood within the re-entrant angle, and the wing contained chambers. Greenknowe Tower (Borders) is a fine ruined L-plan tower house while Craigievar (Grampian) is complete.

The defensive features became less obvious. Larger windows were still protected by iron yetts or grills, and gunloops became ornamental. Open rounds were replaced by bartizans, with conical roofs and parapets were covered. Decorative features, as well as heraldic panels, inscribed lintels, tempera painting and modelled plaster work were introduced. These design features showed French and Italian influences. The tower usually had a small courtyard with ranges of buildings, including a brewhouse, stabling and more accommodation.

The basement was vaulted and contained a kitchen with a large fireplace, a wine-cellar with a small stair to the hall above, and other cellars. The hall was on the first floor of the main block with private chambers on the floors above and within the garret or attic storey.

Z-plan Tower Houses

(late 16th century)

A variation of the L-plan, a Z-plan tower house consisted of a main block, with two towers at diagonally opposite corners. One of the towers usually housed a stair, while the other provided more accommodation. Often further wings or ranges were added to the tower, making it E-plan.

Glenbuchat Castle (Grampian) is a fine example of a ruined Z-plan tower house, as is Drochil Castle (Borders), while Claypotts Castle (Tayside) is still roofed.

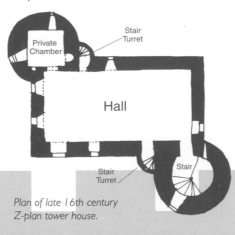

Plan of late 16th century Z-plan tower house.

Forts *(16th/17th/18th century)*

With the advent of more sophisticated artillery, the castle became increasingly redundant as a major defensive structure. As early as the 1540s, forts were being built to withstand attack by cannon. The English constructed forts, during the invasion of Scotland in 1547-50, including those at Roxburgh (Borders), Eyemouth (Borders) and Haddington (Lothian), which consisted of ramparts and bastions of earth rather than high walls. In the 1650s Cromwell built forts such as those at Ayr, Leith (Lothian), Perth, Inverlochy (Highland) and Aberdeen. The Hanoverian Government built forts, barracks and roads after the Jacobite Risings of 1715 and 1745, including those at Fort George, Fort William, Fort Augustus and Ruthven Barracks (all Highland). Other castles such as Corgarff and Braemar (Grampian) were given artillery bastions and were used as bases for campaigns against illicit whisky distilling in the late 18th century.

Castellated Mansion Houses

Even before the Jacobite Risings, most houses had ceased to be fortified. By the mid-18th century, most new houses were built in a classical, palladian or symmetrical style, designed by architects such as Robert Adam. Many castles were abandoned at this time, because they were uncomfortable and unfashionable as dwellings – many landowners wishing to forget their unruly and barbaric past.

Edzell Castle (Tower House).

In the 19th century baronial mansions came into fashion, incorporating or recreating mock castellated features such as towers and turrets, corbelling and machiolations. Castles were reused, restored and reoccupied. Architects such as William Burn and David Bryce in the 19th century, and Sir Robert Lorimer in the 20th century, designed these castellated mansions. Many of these large country houses did not survive use by the government in World War II. The fashion for restoring and living in many of the smaller towers and fortified houses has greatly increased in recent years.

Extract from "The Castles of Scotland" (second edition) by MARTIN COVENTRY
ISBN: 1 899874 10 0
Published by: Goblinshead

APRIL

● **4**
Stirling Castle
Gaddgedlar & Edinburgh Bird of Prey Centre – living history, combat re-enactment and falconry (12 – 4pm).

● **4**
Traquair
Easter Egg Extravaganza.

● **17 – 18**
Brodie Castle
Daffodil Centenary Show & Exhibition.

● **24 – 25**
Kelburn Castle
Woodcraft & Forestry Fair.

MAY

● **9**
Kelburn Castle
Dog Show & Gymkhana.

● **29**
Blair Castle
Annual Parade of the Atholl Highlanders.

● **29 – 30**
Traquair
Scottish Beer Festival.

● **29 – 31**
Kelburn Castle
Festival of Flight.

● **30**
Blair Castle
Annual Highland Games.

● **30**
Stirling Castle
The Clann – fight display group, 2.15pm & 3.45pm.

JUNE

● **5 – 7**
Cawdor Castle
Special Garden Weekend.

● **12 – 13**
Tantallon Castle
Medieval Jousting.

● **14**
Stirling Castle
Falconry Hierarchy (11am–4pm).

● **15 – 29** (Tuesdays & Saturdays)
Stirling Castle
Heritage Events Company in Mary's Day – everyday life during the reign of Mary Queen of Scots. (11am – 4pm).

● **16 – 30** (Wednesdays)
Stirling Castle
Alba Adventure Company present "A Jacobite Soldier" (10am – 4pm).

● **17**
Stirling Castle
British Birds of Prey (11am – 4pm).

● **18 – 25** (Fridays)
Stirling Castle
Alba Adventure Company present "Life of a Redcoat Soldier" (10am – 4pm).

● **21**
Stirling Castle
Raptors – visit the display of buzzards, hawks and falcons (11am – 4pm).

● **24**
Stirling Castle
The World of Owls (11am – 4pm).

JULY

● **1**
Stirling Castle
British Birds of Prey (11am – 4pm).

● **2 – 30** (Fridays)
Stirling Castle
Alba Adventure Company present "Life of a Redcoat Soldier" (10am – 4pm).

● **3 – 31** (Tuesdays & Saturdays)
Stirling Castle
Heritage Events Company in Mary's Day – everyday life during the reign of Mary Queen of Scots. (11am – 4pm).

● **4**
Linlithgow Palace
Traditional Cooking Demonstration.

● **5**
Stirling Castle
Raptors – visit the display of buzzards, hawks and falcons (11am – 4pm).

● **8**
Stirling Castle
The World of Owls (11am – 4pm).

● **9 – 11**
Drumlanrig Castle
Carriage Driving Trials.

● **10 – 11**
Glamis Castle
Strathmore Vintage Vehicle Extravaganza.

● **12**
Stirling Castle
Falconry Hierarchy (11am–4pm)

● **15**
Stirling Castle
British Birds of Prey (11am – 4pm).

● **7 – 28** (Wednesdays)
Stirling Castle
Alba Adventure Company present "A Jacobite Soldier" (10am – 4pm).

● **19**
Stirling Castle
Raptors – visit the display of buzzards, hawks and falcons (11am – 4pm).

● **22**
Stirling Castle
The World of Owls (11am – 4pm).

● **24**
Glamis Castle
Grand Scottish Prom.

● **25**
Melrose Abbey
Traditional Cooking Demonstration.

AUGUST

● **1**
Drummond Castle Gardens
Open Day, 2-5pm, entertainments, teas, raffle.

● **1**
Fort George
Combat re-enactments, living history etc.

● **1 – 8**
Kelburn Castle
"Alice in Wonderland" Dream Week.

● **2**
Stirling Castle
Raptors – visit the display of buzzards, hawks and falcons (11am – 4pm).

● **3 – 31** (Tuesdays & Saturdays)
Stirling Castle
Heritage Events Company in Mary's Day – everyday life during the reign of Mary Queen of Scots

● **4 – 25** (Wednesdays)
Stirling Castle
Alba Adventure Company present "A Jacobite Soldier" (10am – 4pm).

● **5**
Stirling Castle
The World of Owls (11am – 4pm).

● **6 – 27** (Fridays)
Stirling Castle
Alba Adventure Company present "Life of a Redcoat Soldier" (10am – 4pm).

● **7 – 8**
Traquair
Traquair Fair.

● **9**
Stirling Castle
Falconry Hierarchy (11am–4pm).

● **12**
Stirling Castle
British Birds of Prey (11am – 4pm).

● **14 – 15**
Caerlaverock Castle
Battle re-enactment and living history camp.

● **16**
Stirling Castle
Raptors – visit the display of buzzards, hawks and falcons (11am – 4pm).

● **19**
Stirling Castle
The World of Owls (11am – 4pm).

● **23**
Stirling Castle
Falconry Hierarchy (11am–4pm).

● **26 – 29**
Blair Castle
Bowmore Blair Castle Horse Trials.

● **26**
Stirling Castle
Falconry Hierarchy (11am–4pm).

● **29**
Stirling Castle
British Birds of Prey (11am – 4pm).

● **29**
Floors Castle
Massed Pipe Bands Day.

● **29**
Jedburgh Abbey
Traditional Cooking Demonstration.

● **29**
Stirling Castle
British Birds of Prey (11am – 4pm).

● **30**
Stirling Castle
Raptors – visit the display of buzzards, hawks and falcons (11am – 4pm).

SEPTEMBER

● **1 – 15** (Wednesdays)
Stirling Castle
Alba Adventure Company present "A Jacobite Soldier" (10am – 4pm).

● **2**
Stirling Castle
The World of Owls (11am – 4pm).

● **3 – 17** (Fridays)
Stirling Castle
Alba Adventure Company present "Life of a Redcoat Soldier" (10am – 4pm).

● **4 – 18** (Tuesdays & Saturdays)
Stirling Castle
Heritage Events Company in Mary's Day – everyday life during the reign of Mary Queen of Scots (11am – 4pm).

● **5**
Edinburgh Castle
Musical Concert.

● **6**
Stirling Castle
Falconry Hierarchy (11am–4pm).

● **9**
Stirling Castle
British Birds of Prey (11am – 4pm).

● **11 – 12**
Traquair
Traquair Needlework Weekend.

● **12, 19 & 26**
Edinburgh Castle
Musical Concert.

● **13**
Stirling Castle
Raptors – visit the display of buzzards, hawks and falcons (11am – 4pm).

● **16**
Stirling Castle
The World of Owls (11am – 4pm).

OCTOBER

● **1 – 3**
Blair Castle
Special Needlework and Lace Exhibition.

● **30**
Blair Castle
Glenfiddich Piping Championships.

● **31**
Blair Castle
Glenfiddich Fiddling Championships.

The Special Events listed in this index are only a selection of those taking place. You are advised to contact the property direct for exact details, times etc. before making a special journey.

The NPI National Heritage

Awards

Brodie Castle:
The 1998 Scottish Area winner

As you look through the Guide to Historic Properties in Scotland think of the effort and tireless dedication that owners and managers put in towards making their properties exceptionally enjoyable placcs to visit.

NPI, the pensions and retirement specialist, first awarded the prestigious NPI National Heritage Awards to give visitors an opportunity to vote for the properties they had particularly enjoyed and to reward those whose endeavours they felt should receive special recognition.

In 1998 more people than ever submitted NPI National Heritage Awards voting forms giving their views on properties that provided a worthwhile, value-packed and entertaining day out.

The NPI National Hertiage Awards importantly enable you to reward everyone working behind the scenes who invest their time to make such visits special. It is your chance to vote not only for the presentation of the property, gardens and grounds but for the personal touches – the enthusiasm of the staff, the quality of the gift shops.

Although the awards cover the whole of the UK, the 1998 Scottish Area winner, Brodie Castle, near Forres in the Grampian region, perfectly captures the spirit of these awards. A beautiful turreted castle, it contains fine French furniture, English, Continental and Chinese porcelain, and a major collection of paintings ranging from 17th century Dutch to 18th century and early 19th century English watercolours and Scottish colourists. All this though, achieved through the unflagging efforts of dedicated volunteers and employees of the National Trust for Scotland.

The result is a most perfect day out.

Reward your favourite property in 1999

If you would like to reward your favourite property by nominating it for an NPI National Heritage Award, please write to: **Claire Barlow,**
NPI Heritage Awards (GD1E),
NP House,
55 Calverley Road,
Tunbridge Wells,
Kent TN1 2UE

Your name will be added to the mailing list and you will receive a copy of the voting form.

NPI – saving for the future

Founded in 1835, NPI has been providing pensions for over 160 years and has now become one of the UK's leading pensions and retirement specialists, managing more than £11 billion of assets. NPI understands the responsibility of saving for the future and with their long track-record of experience can help you make the most of your retirement planning; ask your financial adviser about NPI or call NPI Membership Services on **0800 174192.**

NPI

PROVIDING PENSIONS SINCE 1835

Borders

Manor Valley. Scottish Borders Tourist Board.

'The Pink Boy' - Sir Joshua Reynolds

Owner: His Grace the
Duke of Buccleuch &
Queensberry KT

CONTACT

Mrs P Gray
Buccleuch Heritage Trust
Bowhill House &
Country Park
Bowhill
Selkirk
TD7 5ET

Tel/Fax: 01750 22204

LOCATION

OS Ref. NT426 278

3m W of Selkirk off A708
Moffat Road,
A68 from Newcastle,
A7 from Carlisle
or Edinburgh.

Bus: 3m Selkirk.

Taxi: 01750 20354.

BOWHILL HOUSE & COUNTRY PARK
Selkirk

Scottish Borders home of the Duke and
Duchess of Buccleuch, dating mainly from
1812 and christened 'Sweet Bowhill' by
Sir Walter Scott in his *Lay of the Last Minstrel.*

Many of the works of art were collected by
earlier Montagus, Douglases and Scotts or
given by Charles II to his natural son James,
Duke of Monmouth and Buccleuch. Paintings
include Canaletto's *Whitehall*, works by
Guardi, Claude, Ruysdael, Gainsborough,
Raeburn, Reynolds, Van Dyck and Wilkie.
Superb French furniture, Meissen and Sèvres
porcelain, silver and tapestries.

Historical relics include Monmouth's saddle
and execution shirt, Sir Walter Scott's plaid and

some proof editions, Queen Victoria's letters
and gifts to successive Duchesses of Buccleuch,
her Mistresses of the Robes.

There is also a completely restored Victorian
Kitchen, 19th century horse-drawn fire engine,
'Bowhill Little Theatre', a lively centre for the
performing arts and where, prior to touring
the house, visitors can see 'The Quest for
Bowhill', a 20 minute audio-visual presentation
by Dr Colin Thompson.

Conference centre, arts courses, literary
lunches, education service, visitor centre. Shop,
tearoom, adventure playground, woodland
walks, nature trails, picnic areas. Garden and
landscape designed by John Gilpin.

❖

Fashion shows, air
displays, archery, clay pigeon
shooting, equestrian events, charity garden parties, shows, rallies,
filming, lecture theatre. House is
open by appointment outside
public hours to groups led by
officials of a recognised museum,
gallery or educational establish-
ment. No photography inside
house.

Inside caterers normally used
but outside caterers considered.

Visitors may alight at entrance.
WC. Wheelchair visitors free.

Groups can book in advance
(special rates), menus on request.

For groups. Tour time 1¼ hrs.

60 cars and 6 coaches within
50yds of house.

Welcome. Projects in Bowhill
House and Victorian kitchen,
Education Officers (service
provided free of charge), schoolroom, ranger-led nature walks,
adventure playground.

On leads.

'Winter' - Sir Joshua Reynolds

OPENING TIMES

SUMMER
24 April - 30 August

Country Park
Daily except Fris
(open Fris in July)
12 noon - 5pm.

House
1 - 31 July
Daily: 1 - 4.30pm.

WINTER
By appointment only,
for educational groups.

ADMISSION

SUMMER

House & Country Park
Adult £4.50
Child (5-16yrs) £2.00
OAP/Student...........£4.00
Group (20+)..............£4.00
Wheelchair visitors ..Free

Country Park only
All ages......................£2.00

WINTER

House & Country Park
Adult £6.00
Child (5-16yrs) £2.00

Pre-booked educational
groups (20+) persons
welcomed.

FLOORS CASTLE
Kelso

FLOORS CASTLE, home of the Duke and Duchess of Roxburghe, is situated in the heart of the Scottish Border Country. It is reputedly the largest inhabited castle in Scotland. Designed by William Adam, who was both masterbuilder and architect, for the first Duke of Roxburghe, building started in 1721.

It was the present Duke's great-great-grandfather James, the 6th Duke, who embellished the plain Adam features of the building. In about 1849 Playfair, letting his imagination and talent run riot, transformed the Castle, creating a multitude of spires and domes.

The apartments now display the outstanding collection of French 17th and 18th century furniture, magnificent tapestries, Chinese and European porcelain and many other fine works of art. Many of the treasures in the castle today were collected by Duchess May, American wife of the 8th Duke.

The castle has been seen on cinema screens worldwide in the film *Greystoke*, as the home of Tarzan, the Earl of Greystoke.

Gardens
The extensive parkland and gardens overlooking the Tweed provide a variety of wooded walks. The walled garden contains splendid herbaceous borders and in the outer walled garden a summerhouse built for Queen Victoria's visit in 1867 can still be seen. An excellent children's playground and picnic area are very close to the castle.

Owner: His Grace the Duke of Roxburghe

CONTACT

Philip Massey
Director of Operations
Roxburghe Estates Office
Kelso
Roxburghshire
Scotland
TD5 7SF

Tel: 01573 223333

Fax: 01573 226056

LOCATION

OS Ref. NT711 347

From South A68, A698.

From North A68, A697/9
In Kelso follow signs.

Bus: Kelso Bus Station 1m.

Rail: Berwick 20m.

OPENING TIMES

SUMMER
2 April - 31 October
Daily: 10am - 4.30pm.

Last admission 4pm.

WINTER
November - March
Closed to the general public, available for events.

ADMISSION

SUMMER

Adult	£5.00
Child (5 - 15yrs)	£3.00
OAP/Student	£4.50
Family	£12.00

Groups (min 20)
Adult	£4.00
Child (5 - 15yrs)	£2.50
OAP/Student	£3.75

Grounds only
	£3.00
Groups	£2.50

SPECIAL EVENTS

- **AUG 29:**
Massed Pipe Bands Day.

CONFERENCE/FUNCTION

ROOM	SIZE	MAX CAPACITY
Dining Rm	18m x 7m	150
Ballroom	21m x 8m	150

Gala dinners, conferences, product launches, 4 x 4 driving, incentive groups, highland games and other promotional events. Extensive park, helicopter pad, fishing, clay pigeon and pheasant shooting. No photography inside the castle.

Visitors may alight at the entrance. WC.

Self-service, licensed, seats 125 opens 10am.

By arrangement for up to 100. Tour time 1¼ hrs.

Unlimited for cars, 100 yds away, coach park 50 yds. Coaches can be driven to the entrance, waiting area close to restaurant exit. Lunch or tea for coach drivers.

Welcome, guide provided. Playground facilities.

Guide dogs only.

MANDERSTON
Duns

Owner: The Lord Palmer

CONTACT

The Lord or Lady Palmer
Manderston
Duns
Berwickshire
Scotland
TD11 3PP

Tel: 01361 883450
Secretary: 01361 882636

Fax: 01361 882010

e-mail: palmer@
manderston.demon.co.uk

LOCATION

OS Ref. NT810 544

From Edinburgh
47m, 1hr.
1¹/₂ m E of Duns on
A6105.

Bus: 400 yds.

Rail: Berwick Station 12m.

Taxi: Chirnside 818216.

Airport: Edinburgh or
Newcastle both
60m or 80 mins.

CONFERENCE/FUNCTION

ROOM	SIZE	MAX CAPACITY
Dining Rm	22'x 35'	100
Ballroom	34'x 21'	150
Hall	22'x 38'	130
Drawing Rm	35'x 21'	150

MANDERSTON, together with its magnificent stables, stunning marble dairy and 56 acres of immaculate gardens, forms an ensemble which must be unique in Britain today.

The house was completely rebuilt between 1903 and 1905, with no expense spared.

Visitors are able to see not only the sumptuous State Rooms and bedrooms, decorated in the Adam manner, but also all the original domestic offices, in a truly 'upstairs downstairs' atmosphere. Manderston boasts a unique and recently restored silver staircase.

There is a special museum with a nostalgic display of valuable tins made by Huntley and Palmer from 1868 to the present day. Winner of the AA/NPI Bronze Award UK 1994.

GARDENS

Outside, the magnificence continues and the combination of formal gardens and picturesque landscapes is a major attraction: unique amongst Scottish houses.

The stables, still in use, have been described by *Horse and Hound* as "probably the finest in all the wide world."

❖

Corporate & incentives venue. Ideal retreat: business groups, think-tank weekends. Fashion shows, air displays, archery, clay pigeon shooting, equestrian events, garden parties, shows, rallies, filming, product launches and marathons. Two airstrips for light aircraft, approx 5m, grand piano, billiard table, fox-hunting, pheasant shoots, sea angling, salmon fishing, stabling, cricket pitch, tennis court, lake. Nearby: 9-hole golf course, indoor swimming pool, squash court. No photography in house.

Available. Buffets, lunches and dinners. Wedding receptions.

Special parking available outside the House.

Tearoom (open as house) with waitress service. Can be booked in advance, menus on request.

Included. Available in French. Guides in rooms. If requested, the owner may meet groups. Tour time 1¹/₄ hrs.

400 cars 125yds from house, 30 coaches 5yds from house. Appreciated if group fees are paid by one person.

Welcome. Guide can be provided. Biscuit Tin Museum of particular interest.

Grounds only, on leads.

5 twin, 4 double and 1 single.

OPENING TIMES

SUMMER
Mid-May - end September
Thur & Sun
2 - 5.30pm.

BH Mon, late May
& August
2 - 5.30pm.

Groups welcome all year
by appointment.

WINTER
September - May
Group visits welcome
by appointment.

ADMISSION

(1999 Prices)
House & Grounds
Adult £5.50
Child £2.50
Groups (20+ on open days)
  Per person £4.00
  School child...........£3.00
  (min Student group £60.00)

Grounds only
Including Stables &
Marble Dairy
Adult £3.50
Child £1.50
Groups (20+)
  Per person £3.50

On days when the house is closed to the public, groups viewing by appointment will have personally conducted tours. The Gift Shop will be open. On these occasions reduced party rates (except for school children) will not apply. Group visits other than open days are £5 (min £100). Cream teas on open days only.

ABBOTSFORD HOUSE

MELROSE, ROXBURGHSHIRE TD6 9BQ

Tel: 01896 752043 **Fax:** 01896 752916

Sir Walter Scott purchased the Cartley Hall farmhouse on the banks of the Tweed in 1812. Together with his family and servants he moved into the farm which he renamed Abbotsford. Scott had the old house demolished in 1822 and replaced it with the main block of Abbotsford as it is today. Scott was a passionate collector of historic relics including an impressive collection of armour and weapons and over 9,000 rare volumes in his library.

Location: OS Ref. NT508 343. 35m S of Edinburgh. Melrose 3m, Galashiels 2m.

Opening Times: 16 Mar - 31 Oct: Mon - Sat, & Suns (Jun - Sept only) 10am - 5pm. Also Suns in Mar - May & Oct, 2 - 5pm. Other dates by arrangement.

Admission: Adult £3.50, Child/Student £1.80. Groups: Adult £2.50, Child £1.30.

House suitable. WC. Guide dogs only.

AYTON CASTLE

AYTON, EYEMOUTH, BERWICKSHIRE TD14 5RD

Owner: D I Liddell-Grainger of Ayton **Contact:** The Curator

Tel: 018907 81212 or 018907 81550

Built in 1846 by the Mitchell-Innes family and designed by the architect James Gillespie Graham. Over the last ten years it has been fully restored and is now a family home. It is a unique restoration project and the quality of the original and restored workmanship is outstanding. The castle stands on an escarpment surrounded by mature woodlands containing many interesting trees and has been a film-making venue due to this magnificent setting.

Location: OS Ref. NT920 610. 7m N of Berwick-on-Tweed on Route A1.

Opening Times: 10 May - 13 Sept: Suns, 2 - 5 pm or by appointment.

Admission: Adult £3, Child (under 5yrs) Free.

AIKWOOD TOWER & JAMES HOGG EXHIBITION

Tel: 01750 52253
Fax: 01750 52261

Ettrick Valley, Nr Selkirk TD7 5IIJ

Owner: Lord & Lady Steel of Aikwood **Contact:** Judy Steel

A fine 16 century pele tower and exhibition of James Hogg.

Location: OS Ref. NT419 260. SE side of B7009, 4m SW of Selkirk.

Opening Times: Easter & May - Sept: Tue, Thur & Sun, 2 - 5pm.

Admission: £1.50.

BOWHILL

See page 12 for full page entry.

BUGHTRIG GARDEN

Tel: 01890 840678 **Fax:** 01890 840509

Bughtrig, Coldstream, Berwickshire TD12 4JP

Owner: Major General C A Ramsay **Contact:** The Secretary

Bughtrig is a classic Georgian family house c1785 with later additions. The formal garden is hedged and close to the house, surrounded by fine specimen trees which provide remarkable shelter. Its $2^1/2$ acres contain an interesting combination of herbaceous plants, roses, shrubs, annuals, fruit, vegetables and a tree nursery. Small picnic area.

Location: OS Ref. NT797 447. $^1/4$ m E of Leitholm Village on B6461.

Opening Times: Garden: Jun - Sept: daily, 11am - 5pm. House: by appointment only.

Admission: Adult £2, Child (under 18yrs)/OAP £1. Rates for House or accommodation by arrangement.

Partially suitable. Limited. Guide dogs only.

4 twin bedrooms/3 bathrooms.

DAWYCK BOTANIC GARDEN

Tel: 01721 760254 **Fax:** 01721 760214

Stobo, Peeblesshire EH45 9JU **Contact:** The Curator

Renowned historic arboretum. Follow the landscaped walks to discover Dawyck's secrets. Amongst mature specimen trees – some over 40 metres tall – are a variety of flowering trees, shrubs and herbaceous plants. Explore the world's first Cryptogamic Sanctuary and Reserve for 'non-flowering' plants.

Location: NT168 352. 8m SW of Peebles on B712.

Opening Times: 1 Mar - 31 Oct: daily, 9.30am - 6pm.

Admission: Adult £3, Child £1, Family £7, Conc. £2.50, Group discounts available.

Partially suitable. WC. Limited for coaches. Guide dogs only

DRUMLANRIG'S TOWER

Tel: 01450 373457　**Fax:** 01450 373993

Tower Knowe, Hawick TD9 7JL

Owner: Scottish Borders Council　　　　**Contact:** The Curator

A fortified tower of the 1550s.

Location: OS Ref. NT502 144. In Hawick town centre at W end of the High Street.

Opening Times: Late Mar - Oct: Suns, 12 noon - 5pm. Late Mar - May & Oct: Mon - Sat, 10am - 5pm, Sun, 12 noon - 5pm. Jun & Sept: Mon - Sat, 10am - 5.30pm. Jul & Aug: Mon - Sat, 10am - 6pm.

Admission: Adult £2, Conc. £1. 10% group discount. Free for local residents.

DRYBURGH ABBEY

Tel: 01835 822381

St Boswells, Melrose

Owner: Historic Scotland　　　　**Contact:** The Custodian

The ruins of Dryburgh Abbey are remarkably complete. The burial place of Sir Walter Scott and Field Marshal Earl Haig. Perhaps the most beautiful of all the Border abbeys.

Location: OS Ref. NT591 317. 5m SE of Melrose off B6356. 1 1/2 m N of St Boswells.

Opening Times: 1 Apr - 30 Sept: daily, 9.30am - 6.30pm. Last ticket 6pm. 1 Oct - 31 Mar: Mon - Sat, 9.30am - 4.30pm, Suns, 2 - 4.30pm, last ticket 4pm.

Admission: Adult £2.50, Child £1, Conc. £1.90.

DUNS CASTLE

DUNS, BERWICKSHIRE TD11 3NW

Owner: *Alexander Hay of Duns*　　　**Contact:** *Mrs Aline Hay*

Tel: 01361 883211　**Fax:** 01361 882015

This historical 1320 pele tower has been home to the Hay family since 1696, and the current owners Alexander and Aline Hay offer it as a welcoming venue for individuals, groups and corporate guests to enjoy. They have renovated it to produce the highest standards of comfort while retaining all the character of its rich period interiors. Wonderful lakeside and parkland setting.

Location: OS Ref. NT777 544. 10m off A4. Rail: Berwick station 16m. Airports: Newcastle & Edinburgh, 1 hr.

Opening Times: Not open to the public except by arrangement and for individuals, groups and companies for day or residential stays. Available all year.

Admission: Rates for private and corporate visits, wedding receptions, filming by arrangement.

🛏 4 x 4-poster, 3 x double, 3 x twin (all with bathrooms), 2 single.

FERNIEHIRST CASTLE

JEDBURGH, ROXBURGHSHIRE TD8 6NX

Owner: *The Marquess of Lothian*　　**Contact:** *Mrs J Fraser*

Tel: 01835 862201　**Fax:** 01835 863992

Ferniehirst Castle – Scotland's Frontier Fortress. Ancestral home of the Kerr family. Restored (1984/1987) by the 12th Marquess of Lothian. Unrivalled 16th century Border architecture. Grand Apartment and Turret Library. A 16th century Chamber Oratory. The Kerr Chamber – Museum of Family History. A special tribute to Jedburgh's Protector to Mary Queen of Scots – Sir Thomas Kerr. Riverside walk by Jed Water. Archery Field opposite the Chapel where sheep of Viking origin still graze as they did four centuries ago.

Location: OS Ref. NT653 181. 2m S of Jedburgh on the A68.

Opening Times: Jul: Tue - Sun (closed Mons), 11am - 4pm.

Admission: Adult £3, Child £1.50. Groups (max. 50) by prior arrangement (01835 862201).

📷

♿ Partially suitable. WCs.

🧑 Guided tours only, groups by arrangement.

🅿 Ample for cars and coaches.

🐕 In grounds, on leads.

FLOORS CASTLE

See page 13 for full page entry.

HALLIWELL'S HOUSE MUSEUM
Tel: 01750 20096 **Fax:** 01750 23282

Halliwell's Close, Market Place, High Street, Selkirk

Owner: Scottish Borders Council **Contact:** Ian Brown

Re-creation of buildings, formerly used as a house and ironmonger's shop.

Location: OS Ref. NT472 286. In Selkirk town centre.

Opening Times: Easter - 31 Oct: Mon - Sat, 10am - 5pm, Suns, 2 - 4pm. Jul & Aug: open until 6pm.

Admission: Free.

HARMONY GARDEN
Tel: 01721 722502 **Fax:** 01721 724700

St Mary's Road, Melrose TD6 9LJ

Owner: The National Trust for Scotland **Contact:** Head Gardener

A tranquil garden offering herbaceous and mixed borders, lawns, vegetable and fruit areas. Fine views of Melrose Abbey and the Eildon Hills. Garden set around 19th century house (not open to visitors).

Location: OS Ref. NT549 342. In Melrose, opposite the Abbey.

Opening Times: 1 Apr - 30 Sept: Mon - Sat, 10am - 5.30pm, Suns, 1.30 - 5.30pm.

Admission: £1.

P No parking. ✖ 🌐

HERMITAGE CASTLE
Tel: 01387 376222

Liddesdale, Newcastleton

Owner: Historic Scotland **Contact:** The Custodian

Eerie fortress at the heart of the bloodiest events in the history of the Borders. Mary Queen of Scots made her famous ride here to visit her future husband.

Location: OS Ref. NY497 961. In Liddesdale 5¹/₂ m NE of Newcastleton, B6399.

Opening Times: 1 Apr - 30 Sept: daily, 9.30am - 6.30pm, last ticket 6pm.

Admission: Adult £1.80, Child 75p, Conc. £1.30.

THE HIRSEL GARDENS, COUNTRY PARK & HOMESTEAD MUSEUM

Coldstream, Berwickshire TD12 4LP **Tel:** 01890 882834 **Fax:** 01890 882834

Owner: Lord Home of the Hirsel **Contact:** Peter Goodall, Hirsel Estate Office

Wonderful spring flowers and rhododendrons. Homestead museum and crafts centre. Displays of estate life and adaption to modern farming.

Location: OS Ref. NT838 393. Immediately W of Coldstream off A697.

Opening Times: Grounds: daily, during daylight hours. Museum & Craft Shop: weekdays, 10am - 5pm. Weekends, 12 noon - 5pm.

Admission: Parking charge only, winter £1, Easter - 31 Oct £2.

🏠 Craft shop. ♿ Partially suitable. WC.

JEDBURGH ABBEY

4/5 ABBEY BRIDGEND, JEDBURGH TD8 6JQ
Owner: Historic Scotland *Contact: The Steward*

Tel: 01835 863925

Founded by David I c1138 for Augustinian Canons. The church is mostly in the Romanesque and early gothic styles and is remarkably complete. The award-winning visitor centre contains the priceless 12th century 'Jedburgh Comb' and other artefacts found during archaeological excavations.

Location: OS Ref. NT650 205. In Jedburgh on the A68.

Opening Times: Apr - Sept: daily, 9.30am - 6.30pm. Oct - Mar: Mon - Sat, 9.30am - 4.30pm, Suns, 2 - 4.30pm. Last ticket 30 mins before closing. 10% discount for groups (10+).

Admission: Adult £3, Child £1, Conc. £2.30.

ℹ Picnic area. 🏠 ♿ Partially suitable. WC. **P** 🍴 Free when booked. 🐕 Guide dogs only.

MANDERSTON

See page 14 for full page entry.

MARY QUEEN OF SCOTS' HOUSE
Tel: 01835 863331 **Fax:** 01450 378506

Jedburgh, Roxburghshire

Owner: Scottish Borders Council **Contact:** The Curator

16th century fortified bastel house. Telling the story 'Scotland's tragic Queen'.

Location: OS Ref. NT652 206. In Queen Street between High Street and A68.

Opening Times: Mar - Nov: Mon - Sat, 10am - 4.30pm, Suns, 12 noon - 4.30pm. Jun - Aug: Suns, 10am - 4.30pm.

Admission: Adult £2, Conc. £1. 10% group discount. Free for local residents.

Jedburgh Abbey, Borders.

MELLERSTAIN HOUSE

MELLERSTAIN, GORDON, BERWICKSHIRE TD3 6LG

Owner: The Earl of Haddington   *Contact:* Mr A Ashby

Tel: 01573 410225   **Fax:** 01573 410636   **e-mail:** mellerstain.house@virgin.net

One of Scotland's great Georgian houses and a unique example of the work of the Adam family; the two wings built in 1725 by William Adam, the large central block by his son, Robert 1770-78. Rooms contain fine plasterwork, colourful ceilings and marble fireplaces. The library is considered to be Robert Adam's finest creation. Many fine paintings and period furniture.

Location: OS Ref. NT648 392. From Edinburgh A68 to Earlston, turn left 5m, signed.

Opening Times: Easter weekend (Fri - Mon), 1 May - 30 Sept: daily, except Sats, 12.30 - 5pm. Groups at other times by appointment.

Admission: Adult £4.50, Child £2, Conc. £3.50. Groups (20+) £3.50. Grounds only: £2.

⬛   ♿ Ground floor & grounds suitable.   ▣   🐕 In grounds.   Ⓦ

MELROSE ABBEY

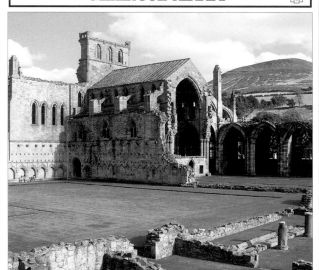

MELROSE, ROXBURGHSHIRE TD6 9LG

Owner: Historic Scotland   *Contact:* The Steward

Tel: 01896 822562

The Abbey was founded about 1136 by David I as a Cistercian Abbey and at one time was probably the richest in Scotland. Richard II's English army largely destroyed it in 1385 but it was rebuilt and the surviving remains are mostly 14th century. Burial place of Robert the Bruce's heart. Local history displays.

Location: OS Ref. NT549 342. In the centre of Melrose off the A68 or A7.

Opening Times: Apr - Sept: daily, 9.30am - 6.30pm. Oct - Mar: Mon - Sat, 9.30am - 4.30pm, Suns, 2 - 4.30pm. Last ticket 30 mins before closing.

Admission: Adult £3, Child £1, Conc. £2.30. 10% discount for groups 10+.

ℹ️ Picnic area.   ⬛   ♿ Tape for visitors with learning difficulties.   🎧   ▣
🐾 Pre-booked visits free.   🐕 Guide dogs only.

MERTOUN GARDENS

Tel: 01835 823236   **Fax:** 01835 822474

St Boswells, Melrose, Roxburghshire TD6 0EA

Owner: His Grace the Duke of Sutherland   **Contact:** Mrs Barnsley

26 acres of beautiful grounds. Walled garden and well-preserved circular dovecote.

Location: OS Ref. NT617 318. Entrance off B6404 2m NE of St Boswells.

Opening Times: Apr - Sept: weekends & Public Holiday Mons only, 2 - 6pm. Last admission 5.30pm.

Admission: Adult £1.50, Child 50p. Groups by arrangement: Adult £1.35, Child 45p.

♿ By arrangement.   ▣   🚫

MONTEVIOT HOUSE GARDEN

Tel: 01835 830380 (mornings only)

Jedburgh, Roxburghshire TD8 6UQ

Fax: 01835 830288

Contact: The Administrator

The river garden planted with herbaceous shrub borders, has a beautiful view of the River Teviot. A semi-enclosed rose garden with a collection of hybrid teas, floribunda and shrub roses. The pinetum is full of unusual trees and nearby a water garden of islands is linked by bridges.

Location: OS Ref. NT648 247. 3m N of Jedburgh. S side of B6400 (to Nisbet). 1m E of A68.

Opening Times: Apr - Oct: daily, 12 noon - 5pm. Coach parties by prior arrangement.

Admission: Adult £2, Child (under 14yrs) Free, OAP £1.

🍴   ♿ Partially suitable. Parking & WCs.   ♿ By arrangement.   ▣
🐕 In grounds, on leads.

NEIDPATH CASTLE

Tel/Fax: 01721 720333

Peebles, Scottish Borders EH45 8NW

Owner: Wemyss and March Estates   **Contact:** The Custodian

Authentic 14th century castle converted to tower house (17th century) home of Fraser, Hay and Douglas families. Pit prison, Laigh Hall with displays, Great Hall with 'Life of Mary Stuart - Queen of Scots' in Batik. Wonderful setting in wooded gorge of River Tweed.

Location: OS Ref. NT237 405. In Tweeddale 1m W of Peebles on A72.

Opening Times: Maundy Thur - 30 Sept: Mon - Sat, 11am - 5pm, Suns, 1 - 5pm. Group bookings only in Oct.

Admission: Adult £2.50, Child £1, Conc. £2, Family (2+3) £6.50. 10% discount for groups (20+). School rate available, 1 teacher free for every 10 children.

⬛   ♿ Ground floor & grounds suitable.   ▣   🐕 In grounds, on leads.

OLD GALA HOUSE

Tel: 01750 20096

Scot Crescent, Galashiels TD1 3JS

Owner/Contact: Mr Ian Brown

Dating from 1583 the former house of the Laird of Gala includes displays on the history of the house and its inhabitants and the early growth of Galashiels. Particularly memorable is the painted ceiling dated 1635.

Location: OS Ref. NT492 357. S of town centre, signed from A7.

Opening Times: Late Mar - early Nov: Tue - Sat, 10am - 4pm.

⬛   ♿ Partially suitable. WCs.   ▣   ♿ By arrangement.   ▣ Limited.
🐕 Guide dogs only.

Melrose Abbey, Borders.

River Tweed. © Scottish Borders Tourist Board

PAXTON HOUSE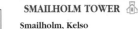

BERWICK-UPON-TWEED TD15 1SZ

Owner: The Paxton Trust   *Contact:* Martin Purslow

Tel: 01289 386291 **Fax:** 01289 386660

'Highly Commended' by the Scottish Tourist Board, 1999. Built in 1756 by John and James Adam, the house boasts the pre-eminent collection of Chippendale furniture on view in Scotland, the largest picture gallery in a Scottish country house, designed by Robert Reid in 1818, which now functions as an outstation for the National Galleries of Scotland, and a fine collection of Regency furniture by Trotter of Edinburgh. Other features include over 80 acres of woodland, parkland, gardens and riverside walks to explore, temporary exhibitions, highland cattle and croquet. Function suite for hire.

Location: OS Ref. NT931 520. 3m off the A1 Berwick-upon-Tweed on B6461.

Opening Times: 1 Apr - 31 Oct: Grounds: 10am - sunset. House: 11am - 5pm. Last house tour 4.15pm. Open to groups/schools all year by appointment.

Admission: Adult £4.50, Child £2.25. Grounds only: Adult £2.25, Child £1.

Conferences, wedding receptions. Partially suitable. Licensed. In grounds, on leads.

PRIORWOOD GARDEN & DRIED FLOWER SHOP

Melrose TD6 9PX   **Tel:** 01896 822493

Owner: The National Trust for Scotland   **Contact:** Mrs Cathy Ross

Overlooked by the Abbey's 15th century ruins is this unique garden, where most of the plants are suitable for drying. With the aid of volunteers, Priorwood Garden markets a wide variety of dried flower arrangements through its own dried flower shop.

Location: OS Ref. NT549 341. In the Border town of Melrose, beside the Abbey.

Opening Times: 1 Apr - 30 Sept: Mon - Sat, 10am - 5.30pm, Suns, 1.30 - 5.30pm. 1 Oct - 24 Dec: Mon - Sat, 10am - 4pm, Suns, 1.30 - 4pm.

Admission: Honesty box £1.

Grounds suitable. WC. No parking. Guide dogs only.

ROBERT SMAIL'S PRINTING WORKS

High Street, Innerleithen, Perthshire EH44 6HA   **Tel:** 01896 830206

Owner: The National Trust for Scotland   **Contact:** Edward Nicol

A printing time-capsule featuring a completely restored Victorian printing works. Visitors can experience the almost forgotten craft of hand typesetting. They will discover the secrets of the printing works from the archive-based posters and see the fully restored machines in action. The buildings also contain the Victorian office with its acid-etched windows, reconstructed waterwheel and many historic items which provide an insight into the history of the Border town of Innerleithen.

Location: OS Ref. NT333 366. In High Street, Innerleithen, 30m S of Edinburgh.

Opening Times: Good Fri - Easter Mon & 1 May - 3 Oct: Mon - Sat, 10am - 1pm & 2 - 5pm, Suns, 2 - 5pm. W/ends in Oct: Sats: 10am - 1pm & 2 - 5pm, Suns, 2 - 5pm. Last admission 45 mins before closing morning or afternoon.

Admission: Adult £2.50, Conc. £1.70, Family £6.70. Groups: Adult £2, School £1.

Ground floor suitable. No parking.

SMAILHOLM TOWER   **Tel:** 01573 460365

Smailholm, Kelso

Owner: Historic Scotland   **Contact:** The Custodian

Set on a high rocky knoll this well preserved 16th century tower houses an exhibition of tapestries and costume dolls depicting characters from Sir Walter Scott's *Minstrelsy of the Scottish Borders*.

Location: OS Ref. NT638 347. Nr Smailholm Village, 6m W of Kelso on B6937.

Opening Times: 1 Apr - 30 Sept: Mon - Sat, 9.30am - 6.30pm, Suns 2 - 4.30pm. Oct & Nov: daily except Thurs afternoons and Fris and Sun mornings, 9.30am - 4.30pm. Last tickets ½ hour before closing.

Admission: Adult £1.80, Child 75p, Conc. £1.30.

THIRLESTANE CASTLE

LAUDER, BERWICKSHIRE TD2 6RU

Owner: Thirlestane Castle Trust   *Contact:* Peter Jarvis

Tel: 01578 722430 **Fax:** 01578 722761
e-mail: thirlestane@great-houses-scotland.co.uk

One of Scotland's oldest and finest castles standing in lovely Border countryside. Thirlestane was the seat of the Earls and Duke of Lauderdale and is still home to the Maitland family. Unsurpassed 17th century ceilings, fine portrait collection, large collection of historic toys, country life exhibitions. Woodland walks. STB commended. MGC Registered. State rooms available for functions.

Location: OS Ref. NT540 473. Off A68 at Lauder, 28m S of Edinburgh.

Opening Times: Easter, 2 - 9 Apr: 11am - 5pm. 1 May - 31 Oct: daily except Sat, 11am - 5pm. Last admission 4.15pm.

Admission: Adult £4.50, Family £11. Groups £3.50. Grounds only £1.50.

By arrangement. In grounds, on leads.

Robert Smail's Printing Works.

TRAQUAIR

INNERLEITHEN, PEEBLESSHIRE EH44 6PW

Owner/Contact: Ms C Maxwell Stuart

Tel: 01896 830323 **Fax:** 01896 830639
e-mail: enquiries@traquair.co.uk

Traquair, situated amidst beautiful scenery and close by the River Tweed, is the oldest inhabited house in Scotland - visited by twenty-seven kings. Originally a Royal hunting lodge, it was owned by the Scottish Crown until 1478 when it passed to a branch of the Royal Stuart family whose descendants still live in the house today. Nearly ten centuries of Scottish political and domestic life can be traced from the collection of treasures in the house. It is particularly rich in associations with the Catholic Church in Scotland, Mary Queen of Scots and the Jacobite Risings.

70 acres of grounds with peacocks, ducks and other wildlife. In spring there is a profusion of daffodils followed by rhododendrons, wild flowers and herbaceous plants. A maze in beech/leylandii cyprus is behind the house.

Location: OS Ref. NY330 354. On B709 near junction with A72. Edinburgh 1hr, Glasgow 1½ hrs, Carlisle 1½ hrs, Newcastle 2½ hrs.

Opening Times: 3 Apr - 30 Sept: daily, 12.30 - 5.30pm. Jun, Jul & Aug: 10.30am - 5.30pm. Last admission 5pm. Oct: Fri - Sun, 12.30 - 5.30pm. Restaurant: open from 11am. Jun, Jul & Aug open from 10.30am.

Admission: House & Garden: Adult £5, Child (under 15yrs) £2.50. Groups: Adult £4.50, Child (under 15yrs) £2 (min payment £100). Garden only: Adult £2, Child (under 15yrs) £1. Winter: Groups: £7, includes glass of wine/whiskey/Traquair Ale and shortbread (min charge £100).

[📷] [ℹ️] No photography in house. [▼] [♿] [☕] Licensed, self-service.

[🎟️] Outside opening hours. [P] Coaches please book. [🐕] In grounds on leads.

[🛏️] 2 four-poster suites, B&B. [WC]

⊙ SPECIAL EVENTS

- **APR 4:** Easter Egg Extravaganza.
- **AUG 7/8:** Traquair Fair.
- **MAY 29/30:** Scottish Beer Festival.
- **SEPT 11/12:** Traquair Needlework Weekend.

Scottish Borders Tourist Board, Harvey Wood.

Scott's View, Nr Melrose.

South West
Scotland

Ayrshire Coast. Ayrshire & Arran Tourist Board. Harvey Wood.

South West Scotland

Christine Ottewill

Owner: James Hunter Blair

CONTACT

James Hunter Blair
Blairquhan Castle
Maybole
Ayrshire
KA19 7LZ

Tel: 01655 770239

Fax: 01655 770278

e-mail: enquiries@
blairquhan.co.uk

LOCATION

OS Ref. NS366 055

From London M6 to
Carlisle, A75 to
Crocketford, A712 to
A713 nr New Galloway,
B741 to Straiton, B7045 to
Ayr. Turn left ¼ m beyond
village. 6m SE of Maybole
off B7045.

Rail: Maybole 7m.

Air: Prestwick Airport,
15m. Direct flights to
London, Belfast & Dublin.
Executive Travel: contact
01655 882666.

CONFERENCE/FUNCTION		
ROOM	SIZE	MAX CAPACITY
Drawing Rms	1200 sq ft	100
Dining Rm	750 sq ft	100
Library	400 sq ft	25
Saloon	600 sq ft	100
Meeting Rm	255 sq ft	50

BLAIRQUHAN CASTLE
Maybole

BLAIRQUHAN is the home of James Hunter Blair, the great-great-grandson of Sir David Hunter Blair, 3rd Baronet for whom it was designed by William Burn and built in 1821-24.

All the Regency furniture bought for the house remains, and the house has not been altered except discreetly to bring it up-to-date. There are ten double bedrooms including four four-poster beds, with en-suite bathrooms, five singles, and many public rooms which can be used for conferences and every sort of occasion.

The castle is approached by a 3 mile private drive along the River Girvan and is situated in one of the most charming parts of south west Scotland. There is a well-known collection of pictures. It is particularly suitable for conferences because the house is entirely at your disposal.

A five minute walk from the Castle are the walled gardens, laid out around the 1800s and recently replanned and replanted.

Blairquhan is only 50 miles from Glasgow. It is within about half an hour's drive of the world-famous golf courses of Prestwick, Troon and Turnberry, the last two of which are venues for the British Open Golf Championships.

❖

Christine Ottewill

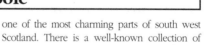 Tree trail, fashion shows, air displays, archery, shooting, equestrian events, garden parties, shows, rallies, filming, grand piano, snooker, fishing. Slide projector, overhead projector, screen, and secretarial assistance for meetings. No photography in castle.

Wedding receptions.

Partially suitable. Visitors may alight at entrance. WC.

Teas, lunches, buffets and dinners. Groups can book in advance, special rates for groups.

By arrangement. Also available in French.

Unlimited.

Guide and schoolroom provided, cost negotiable.

10 doubles (4 4-posters) with bathrooms en-suite, 5 singles. The Dower House at Milton has 10 doubles, 1 single, 6 bathrooms. 7 holiday cottages on the Estate.

In grounds on leads.

OPENING TIMES

SUMMER

17 July - 15 August
Daily (except Mons)
2 - 4.45pm
(Last admission).

Open at all other times by appointment.

WINTER

Open by appointment.

ADMISSION

House & Garden

Adult £4.00
Child (6-16yrs)..........£2.00
OAP.......................£3.00

Groups*
Negotiable

* Minimum payment £20.

SPECIAL EVENTS

- **EVENTS EVERY WEEKEND INCLUDING:**
  Archery
  Model aeroplane flying
  Battle re-enactments.

24

DRUMLANRIG CASTLE
Thornhill

DRUMLANRIG CASTLE, Gardens and Country Park, the home of the Duke of Buccleuch and Queensberry KT was built between 1679 and 1691 by William Douglas, 1st Duke of Queensberry. Drumlanrig is rightly recognised as one of the first and most important buildings in the grand manner in Scottish domestic architecture. James Smith, who made the conversion from a 15th century castle, made a comparable transformation at Dalkeith a decade later.

The castle, of local pink sandstone, offers superb views across Nithsdale. It houses a renowned art collection, including work by Leonardo, Holbein, and Rembrandt, as well as cabinets made for Louis XIV's Versailles, relics of Bonnie Prince Charlie and a 300 year old silver chandelier.

The story of Sir James Douglas, killed in Spain while carrying out the last wish of Robert Bruce, pervades the castle in the emblem of a winged heart. Douglas family historical exhibition. Working forge. The gardens, now being restored to the plan of 1738, add to the overall effect. The fascination of Drumlanrig as a centre of art, beauty and history is complemented by its role in the Queensberry Estate, a model of dynamic and enlightened land management.

❖

Owner: His Grace the Duke of Buccleuch & Queensberry KT

CONTACT

A Fisher
Drumlanrig Castle
Thornhill
Dumfriesshire
DG3 4AQ

Tel: 01848 330248

Fax: 01848 600244

Countryside Service:
01848 331555

e-mail. brc@
drumlanrigcastle.org.uk

LOCATION

OS Ref. NX851 992

18m N of Dumfries,
3m NW of Thornhill
off A76.
16m from M74 at
Elvanfoot.
Approx. 1¹/₂ hrs
by road from Edinburgh,
Glasgow and Carlisle.

No photography inside the castle.

Suitable. WC. Please enquire about facilities before visit.

Snacks, lunches and teas during opening hours.

Adjacent to the castle.

Children's quiz and worksheets. Ranger-led activities, including woodlands and forestry. Adventure playground. School groups welcome throughout the year by arrangement.

In grounds on leads.

OPENING TIMES

SUMMER

Castle

1 May - 15 Aug: daily.
Weekdays: 11am - 4pm,
Suns, 12 noon - 4pm.

16 Aug - 30 Sept by appointment.

Limited tours·
9, 10 & 11 July

**Country Park, Gardens
& Adventure Woodland**

1 May - 30 Sept, daily,
11am - 5pm.

WINTER
By appointment only.

ADMISSION

Castle and Country Park

Adult	£6.00
Child	£2.00
OAP/Student	£4.00
Family (2+4)	£14.00
Disabled in wheelchairs	Free

Pre-booked groups (20+)	
Adult	£4.00
Child	£2.00
Outside normal opening times	£8.00

Country Park only

Adult	£3.00
Child	£1.00

Special Rates
9 - 11 July also Wed & Thur throughout the season.

SPECIAL EVENTS

• **JUL 9 - 11:**
Carriage Driving Trials

CONFERENCE/FUNCTION

ROOM	SIZE	MAX CAPACITY
Visitors' Centre	6m x 13m	50

ARBIGLAND GARDENS

Jarrold Colour Publications

KIRKBEAN, DUMFRIES & GALLOWAY DG2 8BQ
Owner/Contact: Capt & Mrs Beauchamp Blackett

Tel: 01387 880283   **Fax:** 01387 880344

Formal woodland and water gardens which have evolved through three centuries. The ideal family outing garden as the gardens run down to a sheltered sandy bay where the younger members (and dogs) can let off steam. 400 yards from the John Paul Jones Birthplace Museum, his father created the gardens c1750. The photograph is of Arbigland Bay and the House on the Shore at the foot of Arbigland Gardens.

Location: OS Ref. NX990 574. 15m S of Dumfries off A710 'Solway Coast Road'.

Opening Times: 1 May - 30 Sept: Tue - Suns plus BH Mons, 2 - 6pm. House open 22 - 31 May by appointment.

Admission: Adult £2, Child 50p, OAP £1.50, Toddlers Free.

⬜ ♿ Grounds suitable. WC. 📷 🐕 In grounds, on leads.

SPECIAL EVENTS

EASTER - 30 SEPT: John Paul Jones Birthplace Museum open.

BARDROCHAT

COLMONELL, AYRSHIRE KA26 0SG
Owner/Contact: A McEwen

Tel: 01465 881242 **Fax:** 01465 881330

Built by Robert Lorimer in 1893 for the present owner's grandfather. The house stands high on the south side of the Stinchar Valley. The house sleeps up to 16 for garden tours in May, golf on the many local great golf courses or salmon fishing. The price is all inclusive.

Location: OS Ref. NX140 850. Nr Colmonell, 10m S of Girvan off the A77.

Opening Times: Apr - Sept: Mon - Fri, 9am - 5pm.

Admission: Dinner, overnight accommodation, breakfast: £110. Open day prices: Adult £2.50, Child £2.

🍽 ♿ Partially suitable. 👨 By arrangement. 🐕 In grounds, on leads. 🛏 2 single, 6 double all with ensuite bathrooms.

ARDWELL GARDENS   **Tel:** 01776 860227

Ardwell, Nr Stranraer, Dumfries and Galloway

Owner: Mr Francis Brewis   **Contact:** Mrs Terry Brewis

The gardens surround an 18th century house and include a formal garden, wild garden and woodland.

Location: OS Ref. NX102 455. A716 10m S of Stranraer.

Opening Times: 1 Apr - 30 Sept: daily, 10am - 5pm.

Admission: Adult £1.50, Child/Conc. 75p.

🚼 ♿ Partially suitable. WCs. 🅿 Limited parking and poor access for coaches. 🐕 In grounds, on leads.

BACHELORS' CLUB   **Tel:** 01292 541940

Sandgate Street, Tarbolton KA5 5RB

Owner: The National Trust for Scotland   **Contact:** David Rodger

17th century thatched house in which poet Robert Burns and friends formed a debating society in 1780. Burns' mementos and relics, period furnishings.

Location: OS Ref. NS430 270. In Tarbolton, B744, 7½m NE of Ayr, off B743.

Opening Times: Good Fri - 3 Oct: daily, 1.30 - 5.30pm. Weekends in Oct: 1.30 - 5.30pm. Last admission 5pm.

Admission: Adult £2, Conc. £1.30, Family £5.30. Groups: Adult £1.60, School £1.

♿ Ground floor suitable. ✖ 🆃🆆

BARGANY GARDENS   **Tel:** 01465 871249   **Fax:** 01465 871282

Girvan, Ayrshire KA26 9QL

Owner/Contact: Mr John Dalrymple Hamilton

Lily pond, rock garden and a fine collection of hard and softwood trees.

Location: OS Ref. NS250 001. 4m ENE of Girvan by B734. After 2½ m keep ahead on to minor road to Dailly.

Opening Times: 1 Mar - 31 Oct: 10am - 7pm.

Admission: Contributions box.

♿ 🅿 Limited for coaches. 🐕 In grounds, on leads.

BLAIRQUHAN CASTLE 🏛   **See page 24 for full page entry.**

See page 24 for full page entry.

The Ayrshire & Arran Tourist Board

Looking to Arran, South West Scotland.

BRODICK CASTLE & COUNTRY PARK

Harvey Wood

ISLE OF ARRAN KA27 8HY

Owner: The National Trust for Scotland   *Contact:* Veronica Woodman

Tel: 01770 302202   **Fax:** 01770 302312

This is a castle you will never forget! The tall, stately building beckons you with the glow of its warm red sandstone. The setting is staggering, fronted by the sea, bedecked with gardens and overlooked by the majestic mountain of Goatfell. The castle was built on the site of a Viking fortress and dates from the 13th century. The contents are magnificent and include superb silver, porcelain, paintings and sporting trophies. The woodland garden ranks as one of Europe's finest.

Location: OS Ref. NS010 360. Isle of Arran. Ferries from Ardrossan & Claonaig and Kintyre. Ferry enquiries: 01475 650100.

Opening Times: Castle: 1 Apr - 30 Jun & 1 Sept - 31 Oct: daily, 11am - 4.30pm, last admission 4pm. 1 Jul - 31 Aug: daily, 11am - 5pm, last admission 4.30pm. Reception Centre and shop: (dates as castle) 10am - 5pm; restaurant: 11am - 5pm. Garden & Country Park: All year, daily 9.30am - sunset. Goatfell open all year.

Admission: Castle: Adult £5, Conc. £3.40. Groups: Adult £4, School £1, Family £13.50. Garden & Country Park: Adult £2.50, Conc. £1.70. Groups: Adult £2, School £1, Family £6.70.

Suitable. WC. Licensed. In grounds, on leads.

CAERLAVEROCK CASTLE

GLENCAPLE, DUMFRIES DG1 4RU

Owner: Historic Scotland   *Contact:* The Steward

Tel: 01387 770244

One of the finest castles in Scotland on a triangular site surrounded by moats. Its most remarkable features are the twin-towered gatehouse and the Renaissance Nithsdale lodging. The site of two famous sieges. Children's park, replica siege engine and nature trail to site of earlier castle.

Location: OS84 NY025 656. 8m S of Dumfries on the B725.

Opening Times: Apr - Sept: daily, 9.30am - 6.30pm. Oct - Mar: Mon - Sat, 9.30am - 4.30pm, Suns, 2 - 4.30pm. Last ticket sold 30 mins before closing.

Admission: Adult £2.50, Child £1, Conc. £1.90. 10% discount for groups (10+).

Partially suitable. WCs. Limited for coaches. Free if pre-booked. In grounds, on leads.

BROUGHTON HOUSE & GARDEN
Tel/Fax: 01557 330437

High Street, Kirkcudbright DG6 4JX

Owner: The National Trust for Scotland   **Contact:** Frances Scott

This fascinating 18th century house in the pleasant coastal town of Kirkcudbright was the home and studio from 1901 - 1933 of the artist E A Hornel, one of the 'Glasgow Boys'. It contains many of his works, along with paintings by other contemporary artists, and an extensive collection of rare Scottish books, including valuable editions of Burns' works.

Location: OS Ref. NX684 509. Off A/11 / A755, in Kirkcudbright, at 12 High St.

Opening Times: House & Garden: 1 Apr - 31 Oct, daily, 1 - 5.30pm. Last admission 4.45pm.

Admission: Adult £2.50, Conc. £1.70, Family £6.70. Groups: Adult £2, School £1.

Not suitable. By arrangement. Limited.

BURNS' COTTAGE
Tel: 01292 441215

Alloway, Ayrshire KA7 4PY   **Contact:** J Manson

Thatched cottage, birthplace of Robert Burns in 1759. Now a museum.

Location: OS Ref. NS335 190. 2m SW of Ayr.

Opening Times: Apr - Oct: daily, 9am - 6pm. Nov - Mar: daily, 10am - 4pm (Suns, 12 noon - 4pm).

Admission: Adult £2.50, Child/OAP £1.25, Family £6. Admission charge includes entry to Burns' Monument and Gardens.

CARDONESS CASTLE
Tel: 01557 814427

Gatehouse of Fleet

Owner: Historic Scotland   **Contact:** The Custodian

Well preserved ruin of a four storey tower house of 15th century standing on a rocky platform above the Water of Fleet. Ancient home of the McCullochs. Very fine fireplaces.

Location: OS Ref. NX591 553. 1m SW of Gatehouse of Fleet, beside the A75.

Opening Times: 1 Apr - 30 Sept: daily, 9.30am - 6.30pm. Last ticket 6pm. 1 Oct - 31 Mar: Sats, 9.30am - 4.30pm, Suns, 2 - 4.30pm. Last ticket 4pm.

Admission: Adult £1.80, Child 75p, Conc. £1.30.

CARLYLE'S BIRTHPLACE
Tel: 01576 300666

Ecclefechan, Dumfriesshire

Owner: The National Trust for Scotland   **Contact:** The Manager

Thomas Carlyle was born here in The Arched House in 1795, the year before Burns died. Carlyle was a brilliant essayist, historian, social reformer, visionary and literary giant. When he was 14 he walked the 84 miles to Edinburgh University - taking three days. Upstairs is the bedroom in which Carlyle was born. There is also a little museum with a notable collection of photographs, manuscripts and other documents.

Location: OS Ref. NY193 745. Off M74, 6m SE of Lockerbie. In Ecclefechan village.

Opening Times: Good Fri - Easter Mon & 1 May - 30 Sept: Fri - Mon, 1.30 - 5.30pm. Last admission 5pm.

Admission: Adult £2, Child £1.30, Family £5.30. Groups: Adult £1.60, School £1.

Not suitable. By arrangement. Limited.

Burns' Cottage, South West Scotland.

Dean Castle, South West Scotland.

CASTLE KENNEDY GARDENS
Tel: 01776 702024 **Fax:** 01776 706248

Stair Estates, Rephad, Stranraer, Dumfries and Galloway DG9 8BX
Owner: The Earl & Countess of Stair   **Contact:** The Earl of Stair
75 acres of gardens, originally laid out in 1730. Features include rhododendrons, pinetum, walled garden and circular lily pond.
Location: OS Ref. NX109 610. 3m E of Stranraer on A75.
Opening Times: Apr - Sept: daily.
Admission: Adult £3, Child £1, OAP £2.

CRAIGDARROCH HOUSE
Tel: 01848 200202

Moniaive, Dumfriesshire DG3 4JB
Owner/Contact: Mr Alexander Sykes
Location: OS Ref. NX741 909. S side of B729, 2m W of Moniaive, 19m WNW of Dumfries.
Opening Times: Jul: daily, 2 - 4pm.
Admission: £2.

[i] No WC.

CRAIGIEBURN GARDEN
Tel: 01683 221250

Craigieburn House, Nr Moffat, Dumfriesshire DG10 9LF
Owner/Contact: Janet Wheatcroft
A plantsman's garden with a huge range of rare and unusual plants surrounded by natural woodland.
Location: OS Ref. NT117 053. NW side of A708 to Yarrow & Selkirk, 2¹/₂ m E of Moffat.
Opening Times: Easter - Oct: Tue - Sun, 12.30 - 8pm.
Admission: Adult £2, Child Free.

CROSSRAGUEL ABBEY
Tel: 01655 883113

Maybole, Strathclyde
Owner: Historic Scotland   **Contact:** The Custodian
Founded in the early 13th century by the Earl of Carrick. Remarkably complete remains include church, cloister, chapter house and much of the domestic premises.
Location: OS Ref. NS275 083. 2m S of Maybole on the A77.
Opening Times: 1 Apr - 30 Sept: daily, 9.30am - 6.30m. Last ticket 6pm.
Admission: Adult £1.80, Child 75p, Conc. £1.30.

CULZEAN CASTLE & COUNTRY PARK

John K Wilkie

MAYBOLE KA19 8LE
Owner: The National Trust for Scotland   *Contact: Jonathan Cardale*

Tel: 01655 760274   **Fax:** 01655 760615
Robert Adam's 18th century masterpiece, a real 'castle in the air', is perched on a cliff high above the crashing waves of the Firth of Clyde. Arrow slits and mock battlements give medieval touches to the sturdy exterior, and on the seaward-side front is the imposing drum tower. The interior is the epitome of disciplined elegance, crowned by the spectacular oval staircase ascending through ornamental pillars and ironwork balustrading. Adam also designed many interior fittings. The exterior grounds encompass Scotland's first country park.
Location: OS Ref. NS240 100. 12m SW of Ayr, on A719, 4m W of Maybole.
Opening Times: Castle, Visitor Centre, licensed restaurants and shops: 1 Apr - 31 Oct: daily, 10.30am - 5.30pm. Last admission 5pm. Other times by appointment. Country Park: All year, daily 9.30am - sunset.
Admission: Country Park only: Adult £3.50, Conc. £2.50, Family £9. Groups: Adult £3, School coach £20, Family £9. Castle & Park combined ticket: Adult £7, Conc. £5, Family £18. Groups: Adult £6.

  Suitable. WC.  Licensed.   In grounds, on leads.

DALGARVEN MILL
Tel: 01294 552448

Dalry Road, Kilwinning, Ayrshire K13 6PL
Owner: Dalgarven Mill Trust   **Contact:** The Administrator
Water-driven flour mill and country life museum.
Location: OS Ref. NS295 460. On A737 2m from Kilwinning.
Opening Times: All year: Easter - end Oct: Mon - Sat, 10am - 5pm. Suns, 11am - 5pm. Winter closes at 4pm, may not be open Mon/Tue - ring to check.
Admission: Adult £2.50, Conc. £1.50, Family £6.

DEAN CASTLE COUNTRY PARK
Tel: 01563 574916

Dean Road, Kilmarnock, Strathclyde KA3 1XB
Owner: East Ayrshire Council   **Contact:** Andrew Scott-Martin
Set in 81 hectares of Country Park. Visits to castle by guided tour only.
Location: OS Ref. NS437 395. Off A77. 1¹/₄ m NNE of town centre.
Opening Times: Country Park & Visitor Centre: All year. Castle: Easter - end Oct: daily 12 noon - 5pm (last tour 4.15pm). Oct - Easter: weekends only, 12 noon - 4pm (last tour 31.5pm)
Admission: Adult £2.50, Conc. £1.25, Family (2+4) £7. East Ayrshire residents free.

DRUMLANRIG CASTLE
See page 25 for full page entry.

DUNDRENNAN ABBEY
Tel: 01557 500262

Kirkcudbright
Owner: Historic Scotland   **Contact:** The Custodian
Mary Queen of Scots spent her last night on Scottish soil in this 12th century Cistercian Abbey founded by David I. The Abbey stands in a small and secluded valley.
Location: OS Ref. NX749 475. 6¹/₂ m SE of Kirkcudbright on the A711.
Opening Times: 1 Apr - 30 Sept: daily, 9.30am - 6.30pm. Last ticket 6pm. 1 Oct - 31 Mar: Sats, 9.30am - 4.30pm, Suns, 2 - 4pm.
Admission: Adult £1.50, Child 75p, Conc. £1.10.

GALLOWAY HOUSE GARDENS
Tel: 01988 600680

Garlieston, Newton Stewart, Wigtownshire DG8 8HF
Owner: Galloway House Gardens Trust   **Contact:** D Marshall
Created in 1740 by Lord Garlies, currently under restoration.
Location: OS Ref. NX478 453. 15m S of Newton Stewart on B7004.
Opening Times: 1 Mar - 31 Oct: 9am - 5pm.
Admission: Adult £1, Child/Conc. 50p, Family £2.50.

GILNOCKIE'S TOWER
Tel: 01387 371876

Hollows, Canonbie, Dumfriesshire
Owner/Contact: Edward Armstrong
16th century tower house, occupied by the Clan Armstrong Centre.
Location: OS Ref. NY383 787. 2m N of Canonbie on minor road E of A7 just N of Hollows.
Opening Times: Summer months by guided tours: 10am & 2.30pm (closed 11.45am - 2pm).
Admission: Adult £3, Child (under 14yrs) £1.50.

GLENLUCE ABBEY
Tel: 01581 300541

Glenluce
Owner/Contact: Historic Scotland
A Cistercian Abbey founded in 1190. Remains include a handsome 16th century Chapter House.
Location: OS Ref. NX185 587. 2m NW of Glenluce village off the A75.
Opening Times: 1 Apr - 30 Sept: daily 9.30am - 6.30pm. Last ticket 6pm. 1 Oct - 31 Mar: Sats, 9.30am - 4.30pm, Suns, 2 - 4.30pm. Last ticket 4pm.
Admission: Adult £1.80, Child 75p, Conc. £1.30.

GLENWHAN GARDENS
Tel: 01581 400222 **Fax:** 01581 400295

Dunragit, Stranraer, Wigtownshire DG9 8PH
Owner/Contact: Mrs Tessa Knott
Beautiful 12 acre garden overlooking Luce Bay and the Mull of Galloway.
Location: OS Ref. NX150 580. N side of A75, 6m E of Stranraer.
Opening Times: All year: daily, 10am - 5pm.
Admission: Adult £2.50, Child over 14yrs £1, Conc. £2.

[▪]

LOGAN BOTANIC GARDEN
Tel: 01776 860231 **Fax:** 01776 860333

Port Logan, Stranraer, Wigtownshire DG9 9ND

Owner: Royal Botanic Garden Edinburgh   **Contact:** The Curator

Scotland's most exotic garden. Take a trip to the south west of Scotland and experience the southern hemisphere! The exceptionally mild climate allows a colourful array of tender exotics to thrive out of doors - tree ferns, cabbage palms, unusual shrubs, climbers and tender perennials.

Location: OS Ref. NX097 430. 14m S of Stranraer on B7065.

Opening Times: 1 Mar - 31 Oct: daily, 9.30am - 6pm.

Admission: Adult £3, Child £1, Conc. £2.50, Family £7. Group discount available.

◻ ◻ ◻ ◻ Partially suitable. WCs. ◻ Licensed. ◻ By arrangement. **P** ◻ Guide dogs only.

MACLELLAN'S CASTLE
Tel: 01557 331856

Kirkcudbright

Owner: Historic Scotland   **Contact:** The Custodian

A handsome castellated mansion, built in 1577 using stone from an adjoining ruined monastery by the then Provost. Elaborately planned with fine architectural details, it has been a ruin since 1752.

Location: OS Ref. NX683 511. Centre of Kirkcudbright on the A711.

Opening Times: 1 Apr - 30 Sept: daily, 9.30am - 6.30pm. Last ticket 6pm.

Admission: Adult £1.50, Child 75p, Conc. £1.10.

MAXWELTON HOUSE
Tel: 01848 200385

Moniaive, Thornhill, Dumfries & Galloway DG3 4DX

Owner: Maxwelton House Trust   **Contact:** Roderick Stenhouse

Glencairn Castle, now Maxwelton House, dates back to 1370s and was the home of the Earls of Glencairn. Stephen Laurie bought Glencairn Castle in 1611 and changed the name to Maxwelton. Annie Laurie was born here in 1682. The Stenhouse family purchased Maxwelton from the Laurie family in 1968 and carried out one of the largest restorations to a private house within Scotland. The restoration took three years and the continuing labour of no less than 65 men. It was completed in 1972. House, museum, Chapel.

Location: OS Ref. NX822 898. Entrances on B729 near Wallaceton or A702 near Penpont. 13m NW of Dumfries.

Opening Times: Last Sun in May - end Sept: Sun - Fri (closed Sats), 11am - 5pm. Apr/May open for groups only. Last admission 1/2 hr before closing.

Admission: Adult £4, Child (up to 16yrs) £2, Conc. £3. Groups: £3. Garden only: £2.

◻ ◻ ◻ Obligatory. **P** ◻ In grounds, on leads.

NEW ABBEY CORN MILL
Tel: 01387 850260

New Abbey Village

Owner: Historic Scotland   **Contact:** The Custodian

This carefully renovated 18th century water-powered oatmeal mill is in full working order and regular demonstrations are given for visitors in the summer.

Location: OS Ref. NX962 663. 8m S of Dumfries on the A710. Close to Sweetheart Abbey.

Opening Times: 1 Apr - 30 Sept: daily, 9.30am - 6pm. Last ticket 5.30pm. 1 Oct - 31 Mar: Mon - Wed & Sat, 9.30am - 5pm, Thur, 9.30am - 12 noon, Fris closed, Suns, 2 - 4.30pm. Last ticket 4pm.

Admission: Adult £2.30, Child £1, Conc. £1.75. Joint entry ticket with Sweetheart Abbey: Adult £2.80, Child £1.25, Conc. £2.10.

RAMMERSCALES
Tel: 01387 810229/811988 **Fax:** 01387 810940

Lockerbie, Dumfriesshire DG11 1LD

Owner/Contact: Mr M A Bell Macdonald

Georgian house.

Location: OS Ref. NY080 780. W side of B7020, 3m S of Lochmoben.

Opening Times: Last week in Jul, 1st three weeks in Aug: daily (excluding Sats), 2 - 5pm.

Admission: Adult £5, Conc. £2.50.

SHAMBELLIE HOUSE MUSEUM OF COSTUME
Tel: 01387 850375 **Fax:** 01387 850461

New Abbey, Dumfries DG2 8HQ

Owner: National Museums of Scotland   **Contact:** Sheila Watt

Shambellie House is a small country house designed by David Bryce in 1856 for William Stewart. It is set in woodland just outside the village of New Abbey. Inside, in room settings, it displays costume as worn in a country house between 1860 and 1950.

Location: OS Ref. NX960 665. On A710, 7m outside Dumfries on Solway coast road.

Opening Times: 1 Apr - 31 Oct: daily, 11am - 5pm.

Admission: Adult £2.50, Child Free, Conc. £1.50. Season ticket for all National Museums of Scotland sites: Adult £5, Conc. £3.

◻ ◻ No photography in house. ◻ ◻ Not suitable. ◻ ◻ By arrangement. **P** Limited. ◻   In grounds, on leads.

SORN CASTLE
Tel: 01290 551555

Ayrshire KA5 6HR

Owner/Contact: Mrs R G McIntyre

Originally 14th century castle. James V visited the castle then owned by the Earl of Winton in 1598. The castle has been enlarged several times, most recently in 1908.

Location: OS Ref. NS555 265. 4m E of Mauchline on B743.

Opening Times: By appointment.

◻ Grounds suitable. ◻ Obligatory. ◻ In grounds, on leads.

SOUTER JOHNNIE'S COTTAGE
Tel: 01655 760603

Main Road, Kirkoswald KA19 8HY

Owner: The National Trust for Scotland   **Contact:** Ms Jan Gibson

The home of John Davidson, original 'Souter' (cobbler) of Robert Burns' famous narrative poem *Tam O' Shanter*. Burns mementos and restored cobbler's workshop. Life-sized stone figures in adjacent 'ale-house'.

Location: OS Ref. NS240 070. On A77, in Kirkoswald village, 4m SW of Maybole.

Opening Times: Good Fri - 3 Oct: daily, 11.30am - 5pm. Weekends in Oct: 11.30am - 5pm (last admission 4.30pm).

Admission: Adult £2, Child £1.30, Family £5.30. Groups: Adult £1.60, School £1.

◻ House suitable. **P** Limited. ◻ ◻

STRANRAER CASTLE
Tel: 01776 705088 **Fax:** 01776 705835

Stranraer, Galloway

Owner: Dumfries & Galloway Council   **Contact:** John Pickin

Much altered 16th century L-plan tower house, now a museum telling the history of the castle.

Location: OS Ref. NX061 608. In Stranraer, short distance SW of junction between A77 & B737, 1/4 m short of the harbour.

Opening Times: Easter - mid-Sept: Mon - Sat, 10am - 1pm & 2 - 5pm.

Admission: Adult £1.20, Conc. 60p.

SWEETHEART ABBEY
Tel: 01387 850397

New Abbey Village

Owner: Historic Scotland   **Contact:** The Custodian

Cistercian abbey founded in 1273 by Devorgilla, in memory of her husband John Balliol. The principal feature is the well-preserved precinct wall enclosing 30 acres. She also founded Balliol College, Oxford.

Location: OS Ref. NX965 663. In New Abbey Village, on A710 8m S of Dumfries.

Opening Times: 1 Apr - 30 Sept: daily, 9.30am - 6.30pm. Last ticket 6pm. 1 Oct - 31 Mar: Mon - Wed & Sat, 9.30am - 4.30pm, Thurs, 9.30am - 12 noon, Fris closed, Suns, 2 - 4.30pm. Last ticket 4pm.

Admission: Adult £1.20, Child 50p, Conc. 90p. Joint entry ticket with New Abbey Corn Mill: Adult £2.80, Child £1.25, Conc. £2.10.

THREAVE CASTLE
Tel: 01831 168512

Castle Douglas

Owner: The National Trust for Scotland   **Contact:** Historic Scotland

Built by Archibald the Grim in the late 14th century, early stronghold of the Black Douglases. Around its base is an artillery fortification built before 1455 when the castle was besieged by James II. Ring the bell and the custodian will come to ferry you over. Long walk to property. Owned by The National Trust for Scotland but under the guardianship of Historic Scotland.

Location: OS Ref. NX739 623. 2m W of Castle Douglas on the A75.

Opening Times: 1 Apr - 30 Sept: daily, 9.30am - 6.30pm. Last ticket 6pm.

Admission: Adult £1.80, Child 75p, Conc. £1.30. Charges include ferry trip.

THREAVE GARDEN
Tel: 01556 502575 **Tel:** 01556 502683

Castle Douglas DG7 1RX

Owner: The National Trust for Scotland   **Contact:** Trevor Jones

The garden has a wide range of features and a good collection of plants. There are peat and woodland garden plants and a colourful rock garden. Summer months bring a superb show from the herbaceous beds and borders. The heather gardens give a splash of colour, along with bright berries in the autumn. Truly a garden for all seasons.

Location: OS Ref. NX752 605. Off A75, 1m SW of Castle Douglas.

Opening Times: Estate & garden: All year, daily, 9.30am - sunset. Walled garden and glasshouses: all year, 9.30am - 5pm. Visitor Centre, Exhibition, & Shop: 1 Apr - 31 Oct: daily, 9.30am - 5.30pm. Restaurant: 10am - 5pm.

Admission: Adult £4.40, Conc. £2.90. Groups: Adult £3.50, School £1. Family £11.70.

◻ ◻ Grounds suitable. WC. ◻ ◻

WHITHORN PRIORY
Tel: 01988 500508

Whithorn

Owner: Historic Scotland   **Contact:** The Project Manager

The site of the first Christian church in Scotland. Founded as 'Candida Casa' by St Ninian in the early 5th century it later became the cathedral church of Galloway.

Location: OS Ref. NX445 403. At Whithorn on the A746.

Opening Times: Please telephone 01988 500700 for details.

Admission: Joint ticket gives entry to Priory, Priory Museum and archaeological dig.

Edinburgh

Edinburgh
Scotland

Linlithgow Palace. Historic Scotland.

Owner: The Earl of
Rosebery

CONTACT

The Administrator
Dalmeny House
South Queensferry
Edinburgh
EH30 9TQ

Tel: 0131 331 1888

Fax: 0131 331 1788

LOCATION

OS Ref. NT167 779

From Edinburgh A90,
B924, 7m N,
A90 ¹/₂ m.

On south shore
of Firth of Forth.

Bus: From St Andrew
Square to Chapel Gate
1m from House.

Rail: Dalmeny railway
station 3m.

Taxi: Hawes Landing
0131 331 1077
Caledonian Private Hire
0131 331 3321.

DALMENY HOUSE
South Queensferry

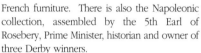

DALMENY HOUSE rejoices in one of the most beautiful and unspoilt settings in Great Britain, yet it is only seven miles from Scotland's capital, Edinburgh, fifteen minutes from Edinburgh airport and less than an hour's drive from Glasgow. It is an eminently suitable venue for group visits, business functions, meetings and special events, including product launches. Outdoor activities such as off-road driving, also feature strongly.

Dalmeny Estate, the family home of the Earls of Rosebery for over 300 years, boasts superb collections of porcelain and tapestries, fine paintings by Gainsborough, Raeburn, Reynolds and Lawrence, together with the exquisite Mentmore Rothschild collection of 18th century

French furniture. There is also the Napoleonic collection, assembled by the 5th Earl of Rosebery, Prime Minister, historian and owner of three Derby winners.

The Hall, Library and Dining Room will lend a memorable sense of occasion to corporate receptions, luncheons and dinners. Alternatively, there are the recently renovated areas of the former kitchen and servants' hall (now named the Rosebery Rooms) and the new Courtyard Restaurant, with facilities specifically designed for business meetings, small conferences, promotions, exhibitions and product launches. A wide range of entertainment can also be provided, from piano recitals to a floodlit pipe band Beating the Retreat.

OPENING TIMES

SUMMER

July and August
Sun, 1 - 5.30pm.
Last admission 4.45pm.

Mon & Tue
12 noon - 5.30pm.
Last admission 4.45pm.

WINTER

Open at other times by
appointment only.

ADMISSION

SUMMER

Adult £3.80
Child (10-16yrs)......£2.00
OAP......................£3.30
Student...................£2.80
Groups (20+)..........£3.00

CONFERENCE/FUNCTION		
ROOM	SIZE	MAX CAPACITY
Library	10.4 x 7m	20
Dining Rm	11.2 x 7.4m	100
Garden Restaurant	12.7 x 9m	200
Rosebery Rooms		150

ℹ️ Fashion shows, product launches, archery, clay pigeon shooting, equestrian events, shows, filming, background photography, small meetings and special events. Lectures on House, contents and family history. Screen and projector. Helicopter landing area. House is centre of a 4¹/₂ m shore walk from Forth Rail Bridge to small foot passenger ferry at Cramond (ferry 9am - 1pm, 2 - 7pm in summer, 2 - 4pm winter, closed Fri). No fires, picnics or cameras.

🍽️ Conferences and functions, buffets, lunches, dinners.

♿ Visitors may alight at entrance. WC.

☕ Teas and lunches, groups can book in advance.

🚶 Special interest tours can be arranged outside normal opening hours.

🅿️ 60 cars, 3 coaches. Parking for functions in front of house.

🚫🐕 No dogs.

Owner: Humphrey &
Rozi Spurway

CONTACT

Rozi Spurway
Harburn House
Harburn
West Calder
West Lothian
EH55 8RN

Tel: 01506 461818

Fax: 01506 416591

e-mail: Harburn@
compuserve.com

LOCATION

OS Ref. NT045 608

Off B7008, 2¹/₂ m S of A71.
2m N of A70. 20m SW of
Edinburgh. Almost
equidistant between
Glasgow and Edinburgh,
within 1hr of Perth,
Stirling, Dundee and the
Border country.

CONFERENCE/FUNCTION		
ROOM	SIZE	MAX CAPACITY
Conference Room	30' x 18'	20
Drawing Rm	30' x 18'	40
Dining Rm	30' x 18'	40
Library	14' x 12'	15
Morning Rm	16' x 15'	20
Whole house		80
Marquee	120' x 40'	500

HARBURN HOUSE
Nr Livingston

HARBURN HOUSE offers its guests the perfect alternative to a first class hotel. This privately owned Georgian mansion, surrounded by its own 3000 acre sporting and leisure estate, is ideally situated offering unparalleled accessibility.

Harburn is essentially small and very personal. It is therefore frequently taken over exclusively for conferences, incentive travel, training seminars and product launches, etc. In this way guests may enjoy the luxury of a five star hotel, combined with the comfort and privacy of their own home.

The policies and lawns of Harburn are ideal for larger events and these can be complemented by our own fully lined and floored marquee.

A stay at Harburn is a very relaxed and informal affair. The staff are first class and the atmosphere is one of a private house party.

The estate provides the full range of sporting and leisure activities including, golf, game shooting, fishing, clay pigeon shooting, tennis, riding and archery to name but a few.

The complete privacy and outstanding scenery, so accessible to the major cities and beauty spots, makes Harburn the ultimate choice for the discerning event or conference organiser.

ℹ️ Filming, conferences, activity days, product launches, golf, riding, fishing, archery, buggies, game shooting, falconry, etc. Golf and Country Club nearby.

🍽 High quality in-house catering by our own top chef and fully trained staff. Prices and menus on request. Wedding receptions.

♿ Ground floor bedroom, dining room and drawing room.

🅿 Parking for 300 cars and 10 coaches in summer, 100+/10 in winter. Follow one way system and 20 mph speed limit, vehicles should not park on grass verges.

🐕 On leads.

🛏 20 bedrooms, all with their own bathrooms, exclusive to one group at a time.

OPENING TIMES

All year by appointment for exclusive use of house and grounds.

ADMISSION

The exclusive use of House and Grounds for activity days (without accommodation).

Per day £700.00

Accommodation Rates
Double with bath
Per person............. £90.00

Dinner, bed & breakfast
Per person............ £110.00

Day Delegate Rate
Per person.............. £40.00

24 hour rate
Per person............ £120.00

VAT is not included in the above rates.

HOPETOUN HOUSE
Edinburgh

HOPETOUN HOUSE is a unique gem of Europe's architectural heritage and undoubtedly 'Scotland's Finest Stately Home' and in 1999 celebrates its 300th anniversary. Situated on the shores of the Firth of Forth, it is one of the most splendid examples of the work of Scottish architects Sir William Bruce and William Adam. The interior of the house, with opulent gilding and classical motifs, reflects the aristocratic grandeur of the early 18th century, whilst its magnificent parkland has fine views across the Forth to the hills of Fife. The house is approached from the Royal Drive, used only by members of the Royal Family, notably King George IV in 1822 and Her Majesty Queen Elizabeth II in 1988.

Hopetoun is really two houses in one, the oldest part of the house was designed by Sir William Bruce and built between 1699 and 1707. It shows some of the finest examples in Scotland of carving, wainscotting and ceiling painting. In 1721 William Adam, by now a renowned Scottish architect, started enlarging the house by adding the magnificent façade, colonnades and grand State apartments which were the focus for social life and entertainment in the 18th century.

The house is set in 100 acres of rolling parkland including fine woodland walks, the red deer park, the spring garden with a profusion of wild flowers, and numerous picturesque picnic spots.

Hopetoun has been home of the Earls of Hopetoun, later created Marquesses of Linlithgow, since it was built in 1699 and in 1974 a charitable trust was created to preserve the house with its historic contents and surrounding landscape for the benefit of the public for all time.

Owner: Hopetoun House Preservation Trust

CONTACT

Lois Bayne Jardine
Hopetoun House
South Queensferry
Edinburgh
West Lothian
EH30 9SL

Tel: 0131 331 2451

Fax: 0131 319 1885

LOCATION

OS Ref. NT089 790

2¹/₂ m W of Forth Road Bridge.

12m W of Edinburgh (25 mins. drive).

34m E of Glasgow (50 mins. drive).

OPENING TIMES

SUMMER

2 April - 26 September
Daily, 10am - 5.30pm
Last admission 4.30pm.

WINTER

October: weekends only, times as above.
Closed at all other times except for group visits by prior arrangement.

ADMISSION

Adult £5.00
Child (5-16yrs)........£2.70
Conc......................£4.50
Group
Adult £4.50
Child (5-16yrs)........£2.20
Conc......................£4.50
Under 5yrs Free.

Winter prices on request.

SPECIAL EVENTS

For a full programme of special events please call on:
0131 331 2451.

CONFERENCE/FUNCTION		
ROOM	SIZE	MAX CAPACITY
Ballroom	92' x 35'	300
Tapestry Rm	37' x 24'	100
Red Drawing Rm	44' x 24'	100
State Dining Rm	39' x 23'	20

Private functions, special events, antiques fairs, concerts, Scottish gala evenings, conferences, grand piano, boules (petanque) piste, croquet lawn, helicopter landing. No smoking or flash photography in house.

Receptions, gala dinners.

Restaurant and exhibitions on ground floor. WC.

Licensed. Groups (up to 250) can book in advance, menus on request tel: 0131 331 4305.

By arrangement. Foreign language guides are usually available.

Close to the house for cars and coaches. Book if possible, allow 1-2hrs for visit (min).

Holders of 2 Sandford Awards for Heritage Education. Special tours of house and/or grounds for different age/interest groups. Teachers' information pack.

No dogs in house but welcome (on leads) in grounds.

ARNISTON HOUSE

GOREBRIDGE, MIDLOTHIAN EH23 4RY

Owner: Mrs A Dundas-Bekker   *Contact: Miss H Dundas-Bekker*

Tel/Fax: 01875 830515

Magnificent William Adam mansion started in 1726. Fine plasterwork, Scottish portraiture, period furniture and other fascinating contents. Beautiful country setting beloved by Sir Walter Scott.

Location: OS Ref. NT326 595. Off B6372, 1m from A7, Temple direction.

Opening Times: 1 Jul - 14 Sept: Sun, Tue & Thur, 2 - 5pm. Guided tours. Pre-arranged groups (10-50) accepted throughout the rest of the year.

Admission: Adult £3, Child under school age Free.

Obligatory. In grounds, on leads.

ARTHUR LODGE
Tel: 0131 667 5163

60 Dalkeith Road, Edinburgh EH16 5AD

Owner/Contact: S Roland Friden

A neo-classical 'Greek Revival' villa, designed by Thomas Hamilton in 1827, Arthur Lodge is a vision of a gentleman's country residence in town. In a beautiful setting, which includes a White Garden and an Italianate sunken garden, the house itself has been imaginatively restored and decorated. Unique in Edinburgh, Arthur Lodge offers visitors the opportunity to experience an exquisite, and often surprising, private residence.

Location: OS Ref. NT268 724. Edinburgh southside, opposite the Commonwealth Pool.

Opening Times: Jun - Jul: Wed & Sat afternoons. Aug - Sept: Weds afternoon only. Tours at 12 noon, 1pm and 2pm. Other times by appointment.

Admission: Adult £3, Conc. £2, including tour.

Obligatory.

BIEL
Tel: 01620 860355

Dunbar, East Lothian EH42 1SY

Owner/Contact: C G Spence

Originally a fortified tower, considerably added to over time.

Location: OS Ref. NJ620 770. 5m from Dunbar on the A1 towards Edinburgh.

Opening Times: By appointment.

Admission: Contribution to charity.

BLACKNESS CASTLE
Tel: 01506 834807

Blackness

Owner: Historic Scotland   **Contact:** The Custodian

One of Scotland's most important strongholds. Built in the 14th century and massively strengthened in the 16th century as an artillery fortress, it has been a Royal castle and a prison armaments depot and film location for *Hamlet*. It was restored by the Office of Works in the 1920s. It stands on a promontory in the Firth of Forth.

Location: OS Ref. NT055 803. 4m NE of Linlithgow on the Firth of Forth, off the A904.

Opening Times: 1 Apr - 30 Sept: daily, 9.30am - 6.30pm, last ticket 6pm. 1 Oct - 31 Mar: Mon - Sat, 9.30am - 4.30pm, last ticket 4pm. Closed Thur pm, Fri & Sun in winter.

Admission: Adult £1.80, Child 75p, Conc. £1.30.

CRAIGMILLAR CASTLE
Tel: 0131 661 4445

Edinburgh

Owner: Historic Scotland   **Contact:** The Custodian

Mary Queen of Scots fled to Craigmillar after the murder of Rizzio and it was here that the plot was hatched for the murder of her husband Lord Darnley. This handsome structure with courtyard and gardens covers an area of one and a quarter acres. Built around an L-plan tower house of the early 15th century including a range of private rooms linked to the hall of the old tower.

Location: OS Ref. NT285 710. 2½ m SE of Edinburgh off the A68.

Opening Times: 1 Apr - 30 Sept: daily, 9.30am - 6.30pm, last ticket 6pm. 1 Oct - 31 Mar: Mon - Sat, 9.30am - 4.30pm, Suns, 2 - 4.30pm, last ticket 4pm. Closed Thur pm & Fri in winter.

Admission: Adult £1.80, Child 75p, Conc. £1.30.

CRICHTON CASTLE
Tel: 01875 320017

Pathhead

Owner: Historic Scotland   **Contact:** The Custodian

A large and sophisticated castle with a spectacular façade of faceted stonework in an Italian style added by the Earl of Bothwell between 1581 and 1591 following a visit to Italy. Mary Queen of Scots attended a wedding here.

Location: OS Ref. NT380 612. 2½ m SSW of Pathhead off the A68.

Opening Times: 1 Apr - 30 Sept: daily, 9.30am - 6.30pm, last ticket 6pm.

Admission: Adult £1.80, Child 75p, Conc. £1.30.

DALKEITH COUNTRY PARK
Tel: 0131 663 5684

Dalkeith, Midlothian EH22 2NJ

Contact: J C Manson

Extensive grounds of Dalkeith Palace. 18th century bridge and orangery. Interpretation area.

Location: OS Ref. NT333 679. 7m SE of Edinburgh.

Opening Times: Mar - Oct: 10am - 6pm.

Admission: Adult/Child £2, Family £7, Groups £1.

Partially suitable. WCs. By arrangement. In grounds, on leads.

DALMENY HOUSE
See page 32 for full page entry.

DIRLETON CASTLE & GARDEN

DIRLETON, EAST LOTHIAN EH39 5ER

Owner: Historic Scotland   *Contact: The Steward*

Tel: 01620 850330

The oldest part of this romantic castle dates from the 13th century, when it was built by the De Vaux family. The renowned gardens, first laid out in the 16th century, now include magnificent Arts and Crafts herbaceous borders and a re-created Victorian Garden. In the picturesque village of Dirleton.

Location: OS Ref. NT516 839. In Dirleton, 7m W of North Berwick on the A198.

Opening Times: Apr - Sept: daily, 9.30am - 6.30pm. Oct - Mar: Mon - Sat, 9.30am - 4.30pm, Suns, 2 - 4.30pm. Last ticket 30 mins before closing.

Admission: Adult £2.50, Child £1, Conc. £1.90. 10% discount for groups (10+).

Partially suitable. Free if booked. Guide dogs only.

DUNGLASS COLLEGIATE CHURCH

Tel: 0131 668 8800

Cockburnspath

Owner: Historic Scotland

Founded in 1450 for a college of canons by Sir Alexander Hume. A handsome cross-shaped building with vaulted nave, choir and transepts.

Location: OS Ref. NT767 719. 1m NW of Cockburnspath. SW of A1.

Opening Times: All year.

Admission: Free.

EDINBURGH CASTLE

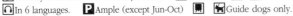

CASTLEHILL, EDINBURGH EH1 2NG

Owner: Historic Scotland   *Contact: Neil Young*

Tel: 0131 225 9846   **Fax:** 0131 220 4733

Scotland's most famous castle, dominating the capital's skyline and giving stunning views of the city and countryside. Home to the Scottish crown jewels, the Stone of Destiny and Mons Meg. Other highlights include St Margaret's Chapel, the Great Hall and the Scottish National War Memorial.

Location: OS Ref. NT252 736. At the top of the Royal Mile in Edinburgh.

Opening Times: Apr - Sept: daily, 9.30am - 6pm. Oct - Mar: daily, 9.30am - 5pm. Last ticket 45 mins before closing.

Admission: Adult £6.50, Child £2, Conc. £5. Pre-booked school visits available free, except Jun - Aug.

Private evening hire of restaurant.
Partially suitable. WCs. Courtesy vehicle. Licensed.
In 6 languages. Ample (except Jun-Oct) Guide dogs only.

Dirleton Castle & Garden, Edinburgh.

THE GEORGIAN HOUSE

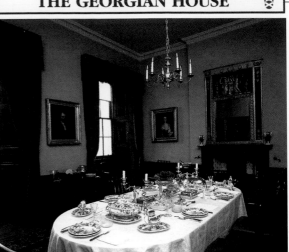

7 CHARLOTTE SQUARE, EDINBURGH EH2 4DR

Owner: The National Trust for Scotland   *Contact: Jacqueline Wyer*

Tel/Fax: 0131 226 3318

The north side of Charlotte Square is Robert Adam's masterpiece of urban architecture - a splendid example of the neo-classical 'palace front'. The three floors of No.7, The Georgian House, are delightfully furnished as they would have been around 1796. There is a fascinating array of china and silver, pictures and furniture, gadgets and utensils from the decorative to the purely functional.

Location: OS Ref. NT247 740. In Edinburgh's city centre, NW of Princes St.

Opening Times: 1 Apr (or Good Fri if earlier) - 31 Oct: Mon - Sat, 10am - 5pm, Suns, 2 - 5pm. Last admission 4.30pm.

Admission: Adult £4.40, Conc. £2.90, Family £11.70. Groups: Adult £3.50, School £1.

No parking.

GLADSTONE'S LAND

Tel: 0131 226 5856   **Fax:** 0131 226 4851

477b Lawnmarket, Royal Mile, Edinburgh EH1 2NT

Owner: The National Trust for Scotland   **Contact:** Pat Wigston

Gladstone's Land was the home of a prosperous Edinburgh merchant in the 17th century. On the Royal Mile, near the Castle, it is decorated and furnished with great authenticity to give visitors an impression of life in Edinburgh's Old Town some 300 years ago. Features of the 6-storey building are the painted ceilings and the reconstructed shop both complete with replicas of 17th century goods.

Location: OS Ref. NT255 736. In Edinburgh's Royal Mile, near the castle.

Opening Times: 1 Apr (or Good Fri if earlier) - 31 Oct: Mon - Sat, 10am - 5pm, Suns, 2 - 5pm, last admission 4.30pm.

Admission: Adult £3.20, Child £2.20, Family £8.60. Groups: Adult £2.60, School £1. Group visits must be booked.

Ground floor suitable. No parking.

GOSFORD HOUSE

LONGNIDDRY, EAST LOTHIAN EH32 0PX
Owner/Contact: The Earl of Wemyss

Tel: 01875 870201 **Fax:** 01875 870376

Robert Adam designed the central block and wings. These wings were later demolished. Two wings were rebuilt in 1890 by William Young. The Big Saloon was burnt in 1940 during military occupation and although it is unrestored, a new roof was constructed in 1987. The south wing (right in photo) is the family home and contains the famous Marble Hall (Staffordshire alabaster). Parts of the south wing are open. There is a fine collection of paintings and works of art. Surrounding gardens are being redeveloped, extensive policies, artificial ponds, greylag geese and other wildfowl breeding. Geese approach house closely.

Location: OS Ref. NT453 786. Off A198 2m NE of Longniddry.

Opening Times: Jun & Jul: Wed, Sat & Sun, 2 - 5pm.

Admission: Adult £2.50, Child 75p.

Grounds suitable. P Limited. In grounds, on leads.

HAILES CASTLE Tel: 0131 668 8800

East Linton

Owner: Historic Scotland

Beautifully-sited ruin incorporating a fortified manor of the 13th century. It was extended in the 14th and 15th centuries. There are two vaulted pit prisons.

Location: OS Ref. NT575 758. 1½ m SW of East Linton. 4m E of Haddington. S of A1.

Opening Times: All year.

Admission: Free.

HARBURN HOUSE See page 33 for full page entry.

HOPETOUN HOUSE See page 34 for full page entry

HOUSE OF THE BINNS Tel: 01506 834255

Linlithgow, West Lothian EH49 7NA

Owner: The National Trust for Scotland **Contact:** Tam & Kathleen Dalyell

A 17th century house, the home of the Dalyells, one of Scotland's great families, since 1612. Here in 1681, General Tam Dalyell raised the Royal Scots Greys Regiment, named after the colour of their uniforms. The house contains fine Italian-style plasterwork and an outstanding collection of family paintings.

Location: OS Ref. NT051 786. Off A904, 15m W of Edinburgh. 3m E of Linlithgow.

Opening Times: House: 1 May - 30 Sept: daily except Fri, 1.30 - 5.30pm, last admission 5pm. Parkland: 1 Apr - 31 Oct: daily, 10am - 7pm. 1 Nov - 31 Mar: daily, 10am - 4pm, last admission 30mins before close.

Admission: Adult £3.90, Conc. £2.60, Family £10.40. Groups: Adult £3.20, School £1. Group visits must be booked.

Ground floor & grounds suitable. WCs. P Limited. Guide dogs only.

INVERESK LODGE GARDEN Tel: 01721 722502 Fax: 01721 724700

24 Inveresk Village, Musselburgh, East Lothian EH21 7TE

Owner: The National Trust for Scotland **Contact:** Head Gardener

Small garden in grounds of 17th century house, with large selection of plants. House closed.

Location: OS Ref. NT348 718. A6124, S of Musselburgh, 6m E of Edinburgh.

Opening Times: 1 Apr - 31 Oct: Mon - Fri, 10am - 4.30pm, Sat & Sun, 2 - 5pm. 1 Nov - 31 Mar: Mon - Fri, 10am - 4.30pm, Suns, 2 - 5pm.

Admission: £1 (honesty box).

Grounds suitable. P Limited.

LAURISTON CASTLE Tel: 0131 336 2060 Fax: 0131 312 7165

Cramond Road South, Edinburgh EH4 5QD

Owner: City of Edinburgh Council **Contact:** Robin Barnes

A beautiful house overlooking the Firth of Forth. The oldest part is a 16th century tower house. William Burn designed the early 19th century additions, which were modernised and furnished around 1900 by the important Edinburgh interior designer William Reid. The Reids also used the house to display their collections of furnishings.

Location: OS Ref. NT203 761. Between Davidsons Mains and Cramond, NW Edinburgh.

Opening Times: 1 Apr - 31 Oct: daily except Fri, 11am - 1pm and 2 - 5pm. 1 Nov - 31 Mar: Sat & Sun, 2 - 4pm. Admission by guided tour only.

Admission: Adult £4, Conc. £3.

Grounds suitable. WC. Obligatory. Guide dogs only.

LENNOXLOVE HOUSE

HADDINGTON, EAST LOTHIAN EH41 4NZ
Owner: His Grace the Duke of Hamilton *Contact:* House Administrator

Tel: 01620 823720 **Fax:** 01620 825112

Home of the Duke of Hamilton. The 14th century keep houses a death mask said to be that of Mary Queen of Scots, a silver casket which once contained incriminating letters that helped send Mary to her death, and a sapphire ring given to her by Lord John Hamilton. The 17th century part of the house contains the Hamilton Palace collection of pictures, furniture and porcelain.

Location: OS Ref. NT515 721. 20m SE of Edinburgh, near Haddington.

Opening Times: Easter - end Oct: Wed, Thur, Sat & Sun, 2 - 4.30pm. Guided tours. Please check if house is open on a Sat before arriving.

Admission: Adult £3.50, Child £1.75. Group charges on application.

i No photography in house. Obligatory. P

LIBERTON HOUSE Tel: 0131 467 7777 Fax: 0131 467 7774
e-mail: ngrarch@aol.com

73 Liberton Drive, Edinburgh EH16 6NP

Owner/Contact: Nicholas Groves-Raines

Built around 1600 for the Littles of Liberton, this harled L-plan house has been carefully restored by the current architect owner using original detailing and extensive restoration of the principal structure. Public access restricted to the Great Hall and Old Kitchen. The restored garden layout suggests the original and there is a late 17th century lectern doocot by the entrance drive.

Location: OS Ref. NT267 694. 73 Liberton Drive, Edinburgh.

Opening Times: 1 Mar - 31 Oct: 10am - 4.30pm, by prior appointment only.

Admission: Free.

Not suitable. P Limited.

Edinburgh Scotland

LINLITHGOW PALACE

LINLITHGOW, WEST LOTHIAN EH49 7AL
Owner: Historic Scotland   *Contact: The Steward*

Tel: 01506 842896

The magnificent remains of a great royal palace set in its own park and beside Linlithgow Loch. A favoured residence of the Stewart monarchs, James V and his daughter Mary Queen of Scots were born here. Bonnie Prince Charlie stayed here during his bid to regain the British crown.

Location: OS Ref. NT003 774. In the centre of Linlithgow off the M9.

Opening Times: Apr - Sept: daily, 9.30am - 6.30pm. Oct - Mar: Mon - Sat, 9.30am - 4.30pm, Suns, 2 - 4.30pm. Last ticket 30 mins before closing.

Admission: Adult £2.50, Child £1, Conc. £1.90. 10% discount for groups (10+).

ℹ️ Picnic area.   📷   🍴 Private evening hire.   ♿ Partially suitable.
🎟️ By arrangement.   🅿️ Cars only.   ▣ Free if booked.   🐕 In grounds, off leads.

NEWLISTON
Tel: 0131 333 3231   **Fax:** 0131 335 3596

Kirkliston, West Lothian EH29 9EB

Owner/Contact: Mrs Caroline Maclachlan

Late Robert Adam house. Costumes on display. 18th century designed landscape, rhododendrons, azaleas and water features. On Sundays tea is in the Edinburgh Cookery School in the William Adam Coach House. Also on Sundays there is a ride-on steam model railway from 2 - 5pm.

Location: OS Ref. NT110 735. 8m W of Edinburgh, 3m S of Forth Road Bridge, off B800.

Opening Times: 1 May - 4 Jun: Wed - Sun, 2 - 6pm. Also by appointment.

Admission: Adult £1, Child/OAP 50p, Student £1.

♿ Grounds suitable.   📷   🐕 In grounds, on leads.

Newliston, Edinburgh,

THE PALACE OF HOLYROODHOUSE

Andrew Holt

HM The Queen

EDINBURGH EH8 8DX
Owner: HM The Queen   *Contact: The Superintendent*

Tel: 0131 556 1096   **Fax:** 0131 557 5256

The Palace of Holyroodhouse, Buckingham Palace and Windsor Castle are the Official residences of the Sovereign and are used by The Queen as both a home and office. The Queen's personal standard flies when Her Majesty is in residence. Furnished with works of art from the Royal Collection, these buildings are used extensively by The Queen for State ceremonies and Official entertaining. They are opened to the public as much as the commitments allow. At the end of the Royal Mile stands the Palace of Holyroodhouse. Set against the spectacular backdrop of Arthur's Seat, Holyroodhouse has evolved from a medieval fortress into a baroque residence. The Royal Apartments, an extensive suite of rooms, epitomise the elegance and grandeur of this ancient and noble house, and contrast with the historic tower apartments of Mary Queen of Scots, which are steeped in intrigue and sorrow. These intimate rooms where she lived on her return from France in 1561, witnessed the murder of David Rizzio, her favourite secretary, by her jealous husband, Lord Darnley and his accomplices.

Location: OS Ref. NT269 739. Central Edinburgh, E end of Royal Mile.

Opening Times: Apr - Oct: daily, 9.30am - 5.15pm. Nov - Mar: daily, 9.30am - 3.45pm. Closed Good Fri, 25 - 26 Dec and during Royal visits. Opening arrangements may change at short notice.

Admission: Adult £5.50, Child (up to 17yrs) £2.70, OAP £4.

📷   ♿ Suitable.   🅿️   ▣   🐕 Guide dogs only.   🅥🅦

Rosslyn Chapel, Nr. Edinburgh.

PARLIAMENT HOUSE

Tel: 0131 225 2595

Parliament Square, Royal Mile, Edinburgh   **Contact:** Reception Desk at Door 11
Supreme Court for Scotland, adjacent exhibition detailing the history of Parliament House and its important features.
Location: OS Ref. NT258 736. In the centre of Edinburgh's Royal Mile.
Opening Times: All year: Mon - Fri, 9am - 5pm.
Admission: Free.

PRESTON MILL

Tel: 01620 860426

East Linton, East Lothian EH40 3DS
Owner: The National Trust for Scotland   **Contact:** Property Manager
For centuries there has been a mill on this site and the present one operated commercially until 1957. While the interior of the mill is exciting, the exterior is extremely evocative and much favoured by artists who come from near and far to paint the attractive old buildings, with their red pantile roofs, fringed by the tranquillity of the mill pond with its ever present ducks.
Location: OS Ref. NT590 770. Off the A1, in East Linton, 23m E of Edinburgh.
Opening Times: Good Fri - Easter Mon, 1 May - 3 Oct: Mon - Sat, 11am - 1pm and 2 - 5pm, Suns, 1.30 - 5pm. Weekends in Oct: 1.30 - 4pm, last admission 20mins before close morning and afternoon.
Admission: Adult £2, Child £1.30, Family £5.30. Group: Adult £1.60, School £1. Group visits must book.

ℹ️ ♿Grounds suitable. WC. 🅿️Limited. 🦮Guide dogs only. NTS

ROSSLYN CHAPEL

Antonia Reeve/RCT

ROSLIN, MIDLOTHIAN EH25 9PU

Owner: *The Earl of Rosslyn*   **Contact:** *Stuart Beattie*

Tel: 0131 440 2159 **Fax:** 0131 440 1979 **e-mail:** rosslynch@aol.com
This most remarkable of churches was founded in 1446 by William St Clair, Prince of Orkney. Set in the woods of Roslin Glen and overlooking the River Esk, the Chapel is renowned for its richly carved interior and world famous apprentice pillar. Visitors to the chapel can enjoy a walk in some of Scotland's most romantic scenery. As Sir Walter Scott wrote,'*A morning of leisure can scarcely be anywhere more delightfully spent than in the woods of Rosslyn*'. The chapel is available for weddings throughout the year.
Location: OS Ref. NT275 630. 6m S of Edinburgh off A701. Follow B7006.
Opening Times: All year: Mon - Sat, 10am - 5pm, Suns, 12 noon - 4.45pm.
Admission: Adult £2.50, Child £1, Conc. £2. 10% discount for groups (20-40).

📷 ♿Chapel. Grounds suitable. WC. 🏪 🅿️Limited for coaches. NTS

ROYAL BOTANIC GARDEN

Tel: 0131 552 7171 **Fax:** 0131 248 2901

20A Inverleith Row, Edinburgh EH3 5LR   **Contact:** Angela Kilday
Scotland's premier garden. Discover the wonders of the plant kingdom in over 70 acres of beautifully landscaped grounds including the world-famous Rock Garden, the Pringle Chinese Collection and the amazing Glasshouse Experience featuring Britain's tallest palmhouse.
Location: OS Ref. NT249 751. Off A902, 1m N of city centre.
Opening Times: Daily (except 25 Dec & 1 Jan): open from 9.30am. Closing: Feb 5pm; Mar 6pm; Apr - Aug 7pm; Sept 6pm; Oct 5pm; Nov - Jan 4pm.
Admission: Free. Donations welcome.

📷 ♿ 🍽️Conference facilities. Wedding receptions. ♿Grounds suitable.
🍴Licensed. 🅟Obligatory. 🅿️ 🚻 🦮Guide dogs only.

ST GILES' CATHEDRAL

Tel: 0131 225 9442 **Fax:** 0131 220 4763

Royal Mile, Edinburgh EH1 1RE
Owner: St Giles' Cathedral   **Contact:** Mrs Kirsty Nicol
St Giles' Cathedral dates from the 12th century and is central to Scotland's turbulent history. This beautiful building was the church of John Knox during the Reformation and has many forms and royal connections. It is notable for its fine stained glass, magnificent organ and the exquisite Thistle Chapel. Guides on duty at all times for formal and informal visits.
Location: OS Ref. NT258 736. In the centre of Edinburgh's Royal Mile.
Opening Times: Easter - Mid Sept: Mon - Fri, 9am -7pm, Sats, 9am - 5pm, Suns, 1 - 5pm. Mid Sept - Easter: Mon - Sat, 9am - 5pm, Suns, 1 - 5pm.
Admission: Admission free - donation of £1 per head suggested.

📷 ♿Partially suitable. 🅟By arrangement. 🅿️Public parking close by.
🦮Dogs welcome.

ST MARY'S CATHEDRAL

Tel: 0131 225 6293 **Fax:** 0131 225 3181

Palmerston Place, Edinburgh EH12 5AW   **Contact:** Cathedral Secretary
Neo-gothic grandeur in the classical new town.
Location: OS Ref. NT241 735. ¹/₂ m W of west end of Princes Street.
Opening Times: 7.30am - 6pm. Sun services: 8am, 10.30am and 3.30pm. Weekday services: 7.30am, 1.05pm and 5.30pm. Sat service: 7.30am.
Admission: Free.

♿Suitable. WCs. 🅿️No parking. 🦮Guide dogs only.

SCOTTISH NATIONAL PORTRAIT GALLERY

Tel: 0131 624 6200

1 Queen Street, Edinburgh EH2 1JD   **Contact:** Hazel Sutherland
Unique visual history of Scotland.
Location: OS Ref. NT256 742. At E end of Queen Street, 300yds N of Princes Street.
Opening Times: All year: Mon - Fri, 10am - 5pm. Suns, 2 - 5pm. Closed 25 & 26 Dec.
Admission: Free.

📷 ♿Suitable. WCs. 🏪 🦮Guide dogs only.

STEVENSON HOUSE

Tel: 01620 823217

Haddington, East Lothian EH41 4PU
Owner: Brown Dunlop Country Houses Trust   **Contact:** Mr A C H Dunlop
The house originally dates from the 13th century with reconstructions in the 16th & 17th centuries. Unique domestic enclosed courtyard house and family home.
Location: OS Ref. NT544 748. 20m from Edinburgh. 1¹/₂ m S of A1, 2m E of Haddington.
Opening Times: 3 Jul - 1 Aug 1999: daily except Fris. Guided tours lasting approx 1 hr at 3pm. Other times by arrangement.
Admission: Adult £2.50, Child (under 14) £1. Garden: £1 (payable into box at gate).

🅟

St Giles' Cathedral, Edinburgh.

TANTALLON CASTLE

BY NORTH BERWICK, EAST LOTHIAN EH39 5PN

Owner: Historic Scotland   *Contact:* The Steward

Tel: 01620 892727

Set on the edge of the cliffs, looking out to the Bass Rock, this formidable castle was a stronghold of the powerful Douglas family. The castle has earthwork defences and a massive 80-foot high 14th century curtain wall. Interpretive displays include a replica gun.

Location: OS67 Ref. NT595 850. 3m E of North Berwick off the A198.

Opening Times: Apr - Sept: daily, 9.30am - 6.30pm. Oct - Mar: Mon - Sat, 9.30am - 6.30pm (but closed Thur pm & all day Fri), Suns, 2 - 4.30pm.

Admission: Adult £2.50, Child £1, Conc. £1.90. 10% discount for groups (10+).

[i] Picnic area.   [O]   [&] Partially suitable.   **P**   [W] Booked school visits free. [W] In grounds, on leads.

WINTON HOUSE

PENCAITLAND, TRANENT, EAST LOTHIAN EH34 5AT

Owner: The Winton Trust   *Contact:* Francis Ogilvy

Tel: 01620 824986   **Fax:** 01620 823961

A masterpiece of the Scottish Renaissance with famous stone twisted chimneys and magnificent plaster ceilings. A family home, still after 500 years with many treasures inside, including paintings by some of Scotland's most notable artists, fine furniture and a family exhibition of costumes and photographs. Specimen trees and terraced gardens.

Location: OS Ref. NT439 695. 14m SE of Edinburgh off the A1 at Tranent. Lodge gates S of New Winton (B6355) and in Pencaitland (A6093).

Opening Times: Open Day 17 Apr: 2 - 6pm & 31 Jul - 29 Aug: weekends only, 1.30 - 5pm and other times by prior arrangement.

Admission: Adult £4.20, Child £2, Conc. £3.50. Groups should pre-book (10+).

[i] Filming, product launches. Pottery.   [X]   [T]   [&] Suitable. WCs.   [cup] [X] Obligatory.   **P**   [W] In grounds, on leads.

SPECIAL EVENTS

THROUGHOUT THE YEAR: Musical evenings, dinners, product launches, etc.

Edinburgh & Lothian Tourist Board

Calton Hill at night

Glasgow & Clyde

New Lanark. Greater Glasgow & Clyde Valley Tourist Board.

KELBURN
Largs

KELBURN has been the home of the Boyle family, later the Earls of Glasgow, since the 13th century and it continues to be used as a family home.

The original Norman Keep was extended in 1580, and the magnificent 1700 William and Mary Mansion House was added by the 1st Earl of Glasgow, whose title was bestowed as reward for his role in the Act of Union. The final addition is the Victorian wing of 1879 with its original William Morris wallpapers.

The essential charm of the castle is its intimate lived-in atmosphere, its varied styles and stunning location.

The beautiful and extensive grounds are used for the Country Centre, and include the dramatic glen with woodland trails, waterfalls, and deep gorges. The peaceful walled garden 'The Plaisance' is dominated by two 1,000 year old yew trees and its exotic shrubs benefit from the Gulf Stream climate. Historical features include the Robert Adam Monument, 18th century Sundial and an Ice House.

For the active, there is horse riding, adventure courses, young children's stockade and soft play area.

The Secret Forest provides a series of exotic follies and fairytale features, "a unique attraction and a delight for all ages".

LOCATION

Owner:
The Earl of Glasgow

CONTACT

David Shields -
Development Manager
Kelburn Castle &
Country Centre
South Offices
Fairlie, Nr Largs,
Ayrshire KA29 0BE

Tel: Country Centre:
01475 568685
Castle: 01475 568204

Fax: Country Centre:
01475 568121
Castle: 01475 568328

e-mail: info@
kelburncastle.com

LOCATION

OS Ref. NS210 580

M8 Edinburgh to Glasgow,
M8 Glasgow to Greenock,
A78 to Largs, 2m S of Largs.

Rail: Largs Station 2m.

Air: Glasgow 25m.
Prestwick Int'national 28m.

Bus: A78 main bus
route to Ayr, stop
adjacent to property.

Taxis: A2B taxis
01475 673976.

CONFERENCE/FUNCTION		
ROOM	SIZE	MAX CAPACITY
Drawing Rm	33' x 24'	70
Dining Rm	30' x 20'	60

Corporate events, clay pigeon shoots, exhibitions, business meetings, conferences, fashion shows, filming, product launches, nature activities and barbecues. Helicopter landing pad. Additional rooms for non-plenary sessions. No photography in house.

Full catering facilities for functions / conferences.

Partially suitable, visitors may alight at entrance. WC. Some stairs.

Licensed restaurant and a tearoom. Groups can book (special rates).

Max. 25, no additional cost, tour time 45 mins. Lectures on castle, grounds and history if booked. Ranger tour of grounds.

Coach passengers can alight at the forecourt, coach park 5-10 mins walk.

Welcome. Teachers free, ratio of 1:10. Ranger service for guided walks and nature activities. Worksheets, pets' corner, pony rides/treks, adventure play areas.

In grounds, on leads.

OPENING TIMES

SUMMER
Castle
July, August & September
Daily tours: 1.45pm, 3pm
& 4.15pm. (Except when
there are afternoon
functions).

Tours can be arranged at
other times of the year.

**Country Centre
& Gardens**
Easter - end October
Daily: 10am - 6pm.

WINTER
Castle
By arrangement only.

Country Centre
End October - Easter
11am - 5pm
Grounds only.

ADMISSION

SUMMER
Castle tours
Per person £1.50
Student...................£1.20
(Does not include entry
to Centre.)

Country Centre
Adult £4.50
Child £3.00
Conc. £2.50
Groups (min 12)
Adult £3.00
Child £2.00
Conc. £1.75

SPECIAL EVENTS

• **APR 24 - 25:**
Woodcraft & Forestry Fair.

• **MAY 9:**
Dog Show & Gymkhana.

• **MAY 29 - 31:**
Festival of Flight.

• **AUG 1 - 8:**
'Alice in Wonderland Dream'
Week

BOTANIC GARDENS

Tel: 0141 334 2422   **Fax:** 0141 339 6964

730 Great Western Road, Glasgow G12 0UE
Owner: Glasgow City Council   **Contact:** The General Manager
Location: OS Ref. NS568 674.
Opening Times: All year: 7am - dusk. For glasshouse opening times please ring.
Admission: Free.

   By arrangement.   **P** No parking.   In grounds, on leads.

BOTHWELL CASTLE

Tel: 01698 816894

Uddingston, Strathclyde
Owner: Historic Scotland   **Contact:** The Custodian
The largest and finest 13th century stone castle in Scotland, much fought over during the Wars of Independence. Part of the original circular keep survives, but most of the castle dates from the 14th and 15th centuries. In a beautiful setting overlooking the Clyde.
Location: OS Ref. NS688 593. 1m NW of Bothwell. At Uddingston off the B7071.
Opening Times: 1 Apr - 30 Sept: daily, 9.30am - 6.30pm, last ticket 6pm. 1 Oct - 31 Mar: Mon - Sat, 9.30am - 4.30pm, Suns, 2 - 4.30pm, last ticket 4pm. Closed Thur pm & Fri & Sat mornings in winter.
Admission: Adult £1.80, Child 75p, Conc £1.30.

BURRELL COLLECTION

Tel: 0141 331 1854

Pollok Country Park, 2060 Pollokshaws Road, Glasgow G2 3EH
Owner: Glasgow Museums   **Contact:** Mr Mark McTee
An internationally renowned, outstanding collection of art.
Location: OS Ref. NS560 615.
Opening Times: All year: Mon - Sat, 10am - 5pm. Suns, 11am - 5pm.
Admission: Free.

  i No photography.   Licensed.   **P**
Guide dogs only.

CHATELHERAULT HUNTING LODGE   **Tel:** 01698 426213 **Fax:** 01698 421532

Ferniegair, Hamilton ML3 7UE
Owner: South Lanarkshire Council   **Contact:** Morvern Anderson
Built for James, 5th Duke of Hamilton, designed by William Adam, completed around 1744. Set in 500 acre country park.
Location: OS Ref. NS737 540. W side of A72, 1¹/₂ m SE of Hamilton.
Opening Times: Mon - Sat, 10am - 5pm. Sun, 12 noon - 5pm (Easter Sun - end Sept, 5pm). Closed Christmas and New Year.

  Partially suitable. WCs.   By arrangement.   **P**
Guide dogs only in house.

COLZIUM HOUSE & WALLED GARDEN

Tel/Fax: 01236 823281

Colzium-Lennox Estate, off Stirling Road, Kilsyth G65 0RZ
Owner: North Lanarkshire Council   **Contact:** Charlie Whyte
A walled garden with an extensive collection of conifers, rare shrubs and trees. Kilsyth Heritage Museum, curling pond, tearoom, picnic tables, pitch and putt, woodland walks.
Location: OS Ref. NS762 786. Off A803 Banknock to Kirkintilloch Road. ¹/₂ m E of Kilsyth.
Opening Times: Walled garden: Easter - Sept: daily, 12 - 7pm. Sept - Mar: Sat/Sun, 12 - 4pm. Pitch and putt: Apr - Sept, daily.
Admission: Free. Charge for pitch and putt.

COREHOUSE

Tel: 01555 663126 or 0131 667 1514

Lanark ML11 9TQ
Owner: The Trustees of the late Lt Col A J E Cranstoun MC   **Contact:** Estate Office
Designed by Sir Edward Blore and built in the 1820s, Corehouse is a pioneering example of the Tudor Architectural Revival in Scotland.
Location: OS Ref. NS882 416. On S bank of the Clyde above the village of Kirkfieldbank.
Opening Times: 5 - 20 Aug: for guided tours at 1 & 2pm. 21 Aug - 8 Sept: for guided tours at 11am & 4pm. Closed Mon & Tue.
Admission: Adult £4, Child (under 14yrs) £2, OAP £2.

CRAIGNETHAN CASTLE

Tel: 01555 860364

Lanark, Strathclyde
Owner: Historic Scotland   **Contact:** The Custodian
In a picturesque setting overlooking the River Nethan and defended by a wide and deep ditch with an unusual caponier, a stone vaulted artillery chamber, unique in Britain.
Location: OS Ref. NS815 463. 5¹/₂ m WNW of Lanark off the A72. ¹/₂ m footpath to W.
Opening Times: 1 Mar - 31 Oct: daily, 9.30am - 6.30pm. Closed Thur pm & Fri in Mar & Oct.
Admission: Adult £1.80, Child 75p, Conc £1.30.

FINLAYSTONE

LANGBANK, RENFREWSHIRE PA14 6TJ
Owner: Mr Arthur MacMillan   *Contact:* Mrs Jane MacMillan

Tel: 01475 540285   **Fax:** 01475 540285
Overlooking the River Clyde, Finlaystone was the home of the Earls of Glencairn for 4 centuries and is now the home of the Chief of the Clan MacMillan. Visitors to this delightful country estate can explore beautiful gardens and woodlands, and have the opportunity to view a unique doll collection in the visitor centre which also houses natural history, Celtic art and Clan MacMillan displays and information. Fun for all the family with children's play areas and ranger service.
Location: OS Ref. NS390 730. On A8, 7m W of Glasgow airport.
Opening Times: Grounds; all year, 10.30am - 5pm. House: Jul: Sun pm guided tours or groups any time by appointment. Refreshments & visitor centre: Apr - Sept: daily, 11am - 4.30pm.
Admission: Grounds: Adult £2.50, Child/Conc. £1.50. Extra for House: Adult £1.50, Child/Conc. £1. 'Dolly Mixture': 50p.

    Ground floor & grounds suitable. WC.   By arrangement.
P   In grounds, on leads.

GLASGOW CATHEDRAL

Tel: 0141 552 6891

Glasgow
Owner: Historic Scotland   **Contact:** The Custodian
The only Scottish mainland medieval cathedral to have survived the Reformation complete. Built over the tomb of St Kentigern. Notable features in this splendid building are the elaborately vaulted crypt, the stone screen of the early 15th century and the unfinished Blackadder Aisle.
Location: OS Ref. NS603 656. E end of city centre. In central Glasgow.
Admission: Free.

GREENBANK

Tel: 0141 639 3281

Clarkston, Glasgow G76 8RB
Owner: The National Trust for Scotland   **Contact:** Mr Jim May
Be allured by the beautiful bronze water nymph 'Foam' whose exquisite form complements the circular pool and surrounding greenery. There are several small gardens including a parterre layout illustrating different aspects of gardening. The larger borders contain a wide range of shrub roses and perennial and annual flowers.
Location: OS Ref. NS563 566. Flenders Road, off Mearns Road, Clarkston. Off M77 and A726, 6m S of Glasgow city centre.
Opening Times: All year: daily, 9.30am - sunset, closed 25/26 Dec & 1/2 Jan. Shop & tearoom: 1 Apr - 31 Oct, daily, 11am - 5pm. 1 Nov - 31 Mar: Sat & Sun, 2 - 4pm. House: 1 Apr - 31 Oct: Sun only 2 - 4pm & during special events (subject to functions in progress).
Admission: Adult £3.20, Conc. £2.20, Family £8.60. Groups: Adult £2.60, School £1.

    Grounds suitable. WC.   In grounds, on leads.

HOLMWOOD HOUSE

The National Trust for Scotland

61 NETHERLEE ROAD, CATHCART, GLASGOW G44 3YG

Owner: The National Trust for Scotland   *Contact:* The Property Manager

Tel: 0141 637 2129

This unique villa has been described as Alexander 'Greek' Thomson's finest domestic design. It was built in 1857-8 for James Couper who owned Millholm Paper Mills. The architectural style of the house is classical Greek and many rooms are richly ornamented in wood, plaster and marble. Conservation work continuing to reveal this decoration.

Location: OS Ref. NS580 593. Netherlee Road, off Clarkston road (off A77 and B767).

Opening Times: 1 Apr - 31 Oct: daily, 1.30 - 5.30pm (last admission 5pm). Access may be restricted at peak times.

Admission: Adult £3.20, Conc. £2.20, Family £8.60. Groups: £2.60.

ⓘ No photography in house.   Ⓣ Ⓟ Limited for coaches.   ✗ Ⓦ

HUTCHESONS' HALL ♛   **Tel:** 0141 552 8391 **Fax:** 0141 552 7031

158 Ingram Street, Glasgow G1 1EJ

Owner: The National Trust for Scotland   **Contact:** Carla Sparrow

Described as one of Glasgow city centre's most elegant buildings, the Hall by David Hamilton, replaced the earlier 1641 hospice founded by George and Thomas Hutcheson. Reconstructed in 1876, the building is now 'A-Listed' as being of national importance.

Location: OS Ref NS594 652. Glasgow city centre, near SE corner of George Square.

Opening Times: Visitor centre/shop/function hall: all year (except BHs & 24 Dec - 6 Jan), Mon - Sat, 10am - 5pm. (Hall on view subject to functions in progress).

Admission: Free.

ⓘ Conferences.   Ⓞ Ⓣ Up to 120.   ♿ Stairlift. WC.   ✗ By arrangement.   Ⓦ

KELBURN CASTLE 🏛   See page 44 for full page entry.

MOTHERWELL HERITAGE CENTRE   **Tel:** 01698 251000

High Street, Motherwell

Owner: North Lanarkshire Council   **Contact:** The Manager

Multimedia exhibition and other displays of local history.

Location: OS Ref. NS750 570.

Opening Times: All year: Mon - Sat, 10am - 5pm. Suns, 12 noon - 5pm. (closed 25/26 Dec & 1 Jan).

Admission: Free.

ⓘ Conferences.   Ⓞ ♿ Suitable. WC.   Ⓟ ▣ ✗ Guide dogs only.

MUGDOCK COUNTRY PARK   **Tel:** 0141 956 6100

Craigallian Road, Milngavie, Glasgow G62 8EL

Owner: Stirling and East Dunbartonshire Councils   **Contact:** Iain Arnott

740 acres. Visitor Centre.

Location: OS Ref. NS560 770. 8m NNW of Glasgow, 1/2 m W of A81.

Opening Times: All year: daily.

Admission: Free. Car park: Summer, 9am - 9pm. Winter, 9am - 5.30pm.

ⓘ Conference facilities.   Ⓞ Ⓣ ▣ ✗ By arrangement.   Ⓟ ▣
✗ In grounds, on leads.

NEWARK CASTLE 🏛   **Tel:** 01475 741858

Port Glasgow, Strathclyde

Owner: Historic Scotland   **Contact:** The Custodian

The oldest part of the castle is a tower built soon after 1478 with a detached gatehouse, by George Maxwell. The main part was added in 1597 - 99 in a most elegant style. Enlarged in the 16th century by his descendent, the wicked Patrick Maxwell who murdered two of his neighbours.

Location: OS Ref. NS329 744. In Port Glasgow on the A8.

Opening Times: 1 Apr - 30 Sept: daily, 9.30am - 6.30pm. Last ticket 6pm.

Admission: Adult £1.80, Child 75p, Conc. £1.30.

NEW LANARK

NEW LANARK MILLS, LANARK, S. LANARKSHIRE ML11 9DB

Owner: New Lanark Conservation Trust   *Contact:* The Development Officer

Tel: 01555 661345 **Fax:** 01555 665738

The historic village of New Lanark is a nominated World Heritage Site. Surrounded by woodlands, and the Falls of Clyde, this cotton-spinning village was founded in 1785 and made famous by social pioneer Robert Owen. Beautifully restored as both a living community and attraction, its history is interpreted in the award-winning Visitor Centre. Accommodation available, please ring.

Location: OS Ref. NS880 426. 1m S of Lanark.

Opening Times: All year: daily, 11am - 5pm (closed 25 Dec & 1/2 Jan).

Admission: Visitor Centre: Adult £3.75, Child/OAP £2.50. Groups: 1 free/10 booked.

ⓘ Conference facilities.   Ⓞ Ⓣ
♿ Partially suitable. WC. Visitor Centre is wheelchair friendly.   ▥
✗ By arrangement.   Ⓟ (5 min walk)   ✗ In grounds, on leads.   ▤

Botanic Gardens, Glasgow.

POLLOK HOUSE

The National Trust for Scotland

POLLOK COUNTRY PARK, POLLOKSHAWS ROAD, GLASGOW

Owner: Glasgow City Council (Managed by The National Trust for Scotland)
Contact: The Property Manager

Tel: 0141 616 6410

The Maxwell family have lived at Pollok since the 13th century. Three earlier castles here were replaced by the present house (c1740) after consultation with William Adam. The house now contains an internationally famed collection of paintings as well as porcelain and furnishings appropriate to an Edwardian house.
Location: OS Ref. NS550 616. In Pollok Country Park, off M77/J1, follow signs for Burrell Collection.
Opening Times: 1 Apr - 31 Oct: daily, 10am - 5pm. 1 Nov - 31 Mar: daily, 11am - 4pm. Closed 25/26 Dec & 1/2 Jan.
Admission: Adult £3.20, Child £2.20, Family £8.60. Groups: £2.60.

No photography in house. Partially suitable. **P**

ST MARY'S CATHEDRAL

Tel/Fax: 0141 339 6691

300 Great Western Road, Glasgow G4 9JB
Contact: Rev Griff Dines
Fine Gothic Revival church by Sir George Gilbert Scott, with outstanding contemporary murals by Gwyneth Leech. Regular concerts and exhibitions.
Location: OS Ref. NS578 669. ¼ m after the Dumbarton A82 exit from M8 motorway.
Opening Times: Mon - Fri, 9.30am - 5pm, Sat, 9.30am - 12 noon. Sun services: 8.30am, 10am, 12 noon & 6.30pm. Weekday services: please telephone. Bookshop: Mon - Fri, 10am - 4pm.

Bookshop. Partially suitable. By arrangement. **P** Limited.
School visits by arrangement

SUMMERLEE HERITAGE PARK

Tel: 01236 431261

Heritage Way, Coatbridge, North Lanarkshire ML5 1QD
Owner: North Lanarkshire Council
Contact: The Manager
STB 'Commended' attraction. 22 acres of industrial heritage including Scotland's only remaining electric tramway; a re-created adit mine and mine workers' cottages; all-weather display hall with working and static machinery; picnic and play area. Ironworks Gallery hosts local and touring exhibitions. Special events held at weekends and during holidays, from April to September.
Location: OS Ref. NS730 650.
Opening Times: All year. Summer, 10am - 5pm. Winter: 10am - 4pm (closed 25/26 Dec & 1/2 Jan).
Admission: Free. Tram ride: Adult 60p, Child 35p.

Conferences. By arrangement. **P**
Guide dogs only. Please telephone for details.

THE TENEMENT HOUSE

Tel: 0141 333 0183

145 Buccleuch Street, Glasgow G3 6QN
Owner: The National Trust for Scotland
Contact: Miss Lorna Hepburn
A typical Victorian tenement flat of 1892, and fascinating time capsule of the first half of the 20th century. It was the home of an ordinary Glasgow shorthand typist, who lived up this 'wally close' for more than 50 years. It is exceptional as the gaslit flat retains many of its original fittings and items such as her mother's sewing machine.
Location: OS Ref. NS583 662. Garnethill (three streets N of Sauchiehall Street, near Charing Cross), Glasgow.
Opening Times: 1 Mar - 31 Oct; daily, 2 - 5pm, last admission 4.30pm. Weekday morning visits by educational and other groups (max 15) by booking only.
Admission: Adult £3.20, Conc. £2.20, Family £8.60. Groups: Adult £2.60, School £1.

Not suitable. **P** Very limited. By appointment.

WEAVER'S COTTAGE

Tel: 01505 705588

Shuttle Street, Kilbarchan, Renfrew PA10 2JG
Owner: The National Trust for Scotland
Contact: Grace Murray
Typical cottage of an 18th century handloom weaver contains looms, weaving equipment and domestic utensils. Attractive cottage garden. Regular weaving demonstrations.
Location: OS Ref. NS402 633. Off A740 (off M8) and A737, at The Cross, Kilbarchan, (nr Johnstone, Paisley) 12m SW of Glasgow.
Opening Times: Good Fri - 3 Oct: daily, 1.30 - 5.30pm. Weekends in Oct: 1.30 - 5.30pm. Last admission 5pm.
Admission: Adult £2, Child £1.30, Family £5.30. Groups: Adult £1.60, School £1.

Glasgow & Clyde Valley Tourist Board

City Chambers, Glasgow.

Perthshire,
Angus and Fife

Rolling fields. Perthshire Tourist Board

BLAIR CASTLE
Pitlochry

BLAIR CASTLE has been the ancient home and fortress of the Earls and Dukes of Atholl for over 725 years. Its central location makes it easily accessible from all major Scottish centres in less than two hours.

The castle has known the splendour of Royal visitations, submitted to occupation by opposing forces on no less than four occasions, suffered siege and changed its architectural appearance to suit the taste of successive generations.

Today 32 rooms of infinite variety display beautiful furniture, fine collections of paintings, arms, armour, china, costumes, lace and embroidery, Jacobite relics and other unique treasures giving a stirring picture of Scottish life from the 16th to 20th centuries.

The Duke of Atholl has the unique distinction of having the only remaining private army in Europe - The Atholl Highlanders.

GARDENS

Blair Castle is set in extensive parklands. Near the car and coach parks, there is a picnic area, a deer park and a unique two acre plantation of large trees known as 'Diana's Grove.' It has been said that "it is unlikely that any other two acres in the world contain such a number of different conifers of such heights and of such small age." A restored 18th century garden re-opened to visitors in 1996.

Owner: Blair Castle Charitable Trust

CONTACT

Geoff G Crerar
Tourism Administrator
Blair Castle
Blair Atholl
Pitlochry
Perthshire
PH18 5TL

Tel: 01796 481207

Fax: 01796 481487

LOCATION

OS Ref. NN880 660

From Edinburgh 80m, M90 to Perth, A9, follow signs for Blair Castle. 1¹⁄₂ hrs. Trunk Road A9 2m.

Bus: Bus stop 1m in Blair Atholl.

Train: 1m, Blair Atholl Euston-Inverness line.

Taxi: Elizabeth Yule, 01796 472290.

OPENING TIMES

SUMMER

1 April - 29 October
Daily, 10am - 6pm
Last admission 5pm.
(Jul & Aug: opens 9.30am).

WINTER

Access by arrangement.

ADMISSION

House & Grounds

Adult	£6.00
Child (5-16yrs)	£4.00
OAP/Student	£5.00
Family	£18.00
Disabled	£2.00

Groups (12-40)	
Adult	£5.00
Child (5-16yrs)	£4.00
Primary School	£3.00
OAP	£4.00
Student	£2.00

Grounds only

Adult	£2.00
OAP/Student	£1.00
Family	£5.00

SPECIAL EVENTS

- **MAY 29:**
  Atholl Highlanders' Parade
- **MAY 30:**
  Blair Castle Highland Games
- **AUG 26 - 29:**
  Bowmore Blair Castle International Horse Trials
- **OCT 1 - 3:**
  Special Needlelace Exhibition
- **OCT 30:**
  Glenfiddich World Piping Championships
- **OCT 31:**
  Glenfiddich Fiddling Championships

FUNCTION		
ROOM	SIZE	MAX CAPACITY
Ballroom	89' x 35'	400
State Dining Rm	36' x 25'	200
Exhibition Hall	55' x 27'	90

Fashion shows, garden parties, equestrian events, shows, rallies, filming, highland and charity balls, piping championships, grand piano, helicopter pad, cannon firing by Atholl Highlanders, resident piper, needlework displays. No smoking.

Buffets, dinners, wedding receptions and banquets.

Visitors may alight at the entrance. WC & wheelchair.

Non-smoking. Seats up to 125.

In English, German and French at no extra cost. Max group size 25, tour time 1¹⁄₂ hrs (max).

200 cars, 20 coaches. Coach drivers/couriers free, plus free meal and shop voucher, information pack.

Nature walks, deer park, children's games and pony trekking.

Grounds only.

GLAMIS CASTLE
by Forfar

GLAMIS CASTLE is the family home of the Earls of Strathmore and Kinghorne and has been a royal residence since 1372. It is the childhood home of Her Majesty Queen Elizabeth The Queen Mother, the birthplace of Her Royal Highness The Princess Margaret and the legendary setting of Shakespeare's play *Macbeth*. Although the castle is open to visitors it remains a family home lived in and loved by the Strathmore family.

The castle, a five-storey 'L' shaped tower block, was originally a royal hunting lodge. It was remodelled in the 17th century and is built of pink sandstone. It contains the Great Hall,

with its magnificent plasterwork ceiling dated 1621, a beautiful family Chapel constructed inside the Castle in 1688, an 18th century billiard room housing what is left of the extensive library once at Glamis, a 19th century dining room containing family portraits and the Royal Apartments which have been used by Her Majesty Queen Elizabeth The Queen Mother.

The castle stands in an extensive park, landscaped towards the end of the 18th century, and contains the beautiful Italian Garden which reflects the peace and serenity of the castle and grounds.

Owner: The Earl of Strathmore & Kinghorne

CONTACT

Lt Col P J Cardwell Moore (The Administrator)
Estates Office
Glamis Castle
Glamis
by Forfar
Angus
DD8 1RJ

Tel: 01307 840393

Fax: 01307 840733

e-mail: glamis@great-houses-scotland.co.uk

LOCATION

OS Ref. NO386 480

From Edinburgh M90, A94, 81m.
From Forfar A94, 6m.
From Glasgow 101m.

Motorway: M90.

Rail: Dundee Station 12m.

Air: Dundee Airport 12m.

Taxi: B Morrison 01575 572988.

CONFERENCE/FUNCTION

ROOM	SIZE	MAX CAPACITY
Dining Rm	84 sq.m.	120
Restaurant	140 sq.m.	100
16th century Kitchens		50

[i] Fashion shoots, archery, clay pigeon shooting, equestrian events, shows, rallies, filming, product launches, highland games, new cricket pavilion, grand piano. No photography in the castle.

Shopping complex.

[T] The State Rooms are available for grand dinners, lunches and wedding receptions.

Disabled visitors may alight at entrance. Those in wheelchairs will be unable to tour the castle but may visit the two exhibitions. WC.

[||] Morning coffees, light lunches, afternoon teas. Self-service, licensed restaurant.

All visits are guided, tour time 50 - 60 mins. Tours leave every 10 - 15 mins. Tours in French, German, Italian and Spanish by appointment at no additional cost. Three exhibitions.

[P] 500 cars and 20 coaches 200 yds from castle. Coach drivers and couriers admitted free. Beware narrow gates; they are wide enough to take buses (10ft wide).

One teacher free for every 10 children. Nature trail, family exhibition rooms, dolls' house, play park. Glamis Heritage Education Centre in Glamis village. Education pack. Winner of Sandford Award in 1997.

In grounds, on leads.

OPENING TIMES

27 March - 31 October
Daily, 10.30am - 5.30pm.

(July - August opens 10am.)

Last admission 4.45pm.

Groups welcome by appointment at other times.

WINTER

By arrangement.

ADMISSION

SUMMER
House & Grounds
Adult	£5.40
Child (5-16yrs)	£2.80
OAP/Student	£4.20
Family	£14.50

Groups (20+)
Adult	£4.90
Child (5-16yrs)	£2.30
OAP/Student	£3.70

Grounds only
Adult	£2.40
Child (5 - 16yrs)	£1.30
OAP/Student	£1.30
Disabled	Free

SPECIAL EVENTS

- **JUL 10 - 11:**
  Strathmore Vintage Vehicle Extravaganza.

- **JUL 24:**
  Grand Scottish Prom.

SCONE PALACE
Perth

SCONE PALACE, on the outskirts of Perth, sits on one of Scotland's most historic sites. The crowning place of Scottish kings including Macbeth and Robert the Bruce, and until its infamous removal by Edward I, home of the Stone of Destiny on the Moothill.

The Palace was built on the ruins of the old Abbey and Bishop's Palace which were destroyed in the Reformation. After a brief spell under the Gowrie family, in 1600 Scone passed to the Murray family who continue to maintain it. Extensively rebuilt by the 3rd Earl around 1804, Scone now houses unique collections of Vernis Martin, French furniture, clocks, 16th century needlework (including pieces by Mary Queen of Scots), ivories, objets d'art and one of the country's finest porcelain collections.

GARDENS
The grounds of the Palace house magnificent collections of shrubs, with woodland walks through the pinetum containing David Douglas' original fir and are home to the new Murray Star Maze. There are Highland cattle and peacocks to admire and an adventure play area for children. Like the Palace, the grounds and wooded parklands that stretch down to the River Tay are available for a variety of events, including corporate and private entertaining.

❖

Owner: The Earl of Mansfield

CONTACT
The Administrator
Scone Palace
Perth
PH2 6BD

Tel: 01738 552300

Fax: 01738 552588

LOCATION
OS Ref. NO114 266

From Edinburgh Forth Bridge M90, A93 1 hr.

Bus: Regular buses from Perth (including open-top tours).

Rail: Perth Station 3m.

Motorway: M90 from Edinburgh.

Taxi: 01738 636777.

OPENING TIMES
SUMMER
2 April - 25 October
Daily: 9.30am - 5.15pm.

Last admission 4.45pm

Evening tours by appointment.

WINTER
26 October - 1 April
By appointment only.

ADMISSION
SUMMER
Palace & Garden
Adult £5.40
Child (5-16)............£3.20
OAP......................£4.60
Family £16.50
Groups (20+)
Adult £4.90
Child (5-16)............£2.70
OAP......................£4.20

Grounds only
Adult £2.70
Child (5-16)............£1.50

Private Tour £30 supplement.

WINTER
Per person................£12.50
(£250 min. payment)

CONFERENCE/FUNCTION		
ROOM	SIZE	MAX CAPACITY
Long Gallery	140' x 20'	200
Queen Victoria's Rm	20' x 20'	35
Drawing Rm	50' x 24'	100

Receptions, fashion shows, war games, archery, clay pigeon shooting, equestrian events, garden parties, shows, rallies, filming, shooting, fishing, floodlit tattoos, product launches, highland games, parkland, cricket pitch, helicopter landing, croquet, racecourse, polo field, firework displays, adventure playground.

Grand dinners in state rooms, buffets, receptions, wedding receptions, cocktail parties.

All state rooms on one level, wheelchair access to restaurants. Visitors may alight at entrance. WC.

Two restaurants. Teas, lunches & dinners, can be booked, menus upon request, special rates for groups.

By arrangement. Guides in rooms, tour time 45 mins. French and German guides available by appointment.

Welcome.

300 cars and 15 coaches, groups please book, couriers and coach drivers free meal and admittance.

In grounds on leads.

SPECIAL EVENTS
• **MAY - SEPT** (Monthly): Horse Trials.

• **APR - SEPT** (Monthly): Perth Hunt Races.

• **JULY:** Scottish Game Conservancy Fair.

ABERDOUR CASTLE

Tel: 01383 860519

Aberdour, Fife

Owner: Historic Scotland   **Contact:** The Custodian

A 14th century castle built by the Douglas family. The gallery on the first floor gives an idea of how it was furnished at the time. The castle has a 14th century tower extended in the 16th and 17th centuries, a delightful walled garden and a circular dovecote.

Location: OS Ref. NT193 854. In Aberdour 5m E of the Forth Bridge on the A921.

Opening Times: 1 Apr - 30 Sept: daily, 9.30am - 6.30pm, last ticket 6pm. 1 Oct - 31 Mar: Mon - Sat, 9.30am - 4.30pm, Suns, 2 - 4.30pm, last ticket 4pm. Closed Thur pm & Fris in winter.

Admission: Adult £1.80, Child 75p, Conc. £1.30.

ANGUS FOLK MUSEUM

Tel: 01307 840288

Kirkwynd, Glamis, Forfar, Angus DD8 1RT   Fax: 01307 840233

Owner: The National Trust for Scotland   **Contact:** Kathleen Ager

Where will you find cruisie lamps, pirn winders, cloutie rugs, bannock spades and a thrawcrook? All these fascinating items, and many more, are to be found in the Angus Folk Museum, one of Scotland's finest. The domestic section is housed in six charming 18th century cottages in Kirkwynd, and the agricultural collection is in the farmsteading opposite. The displays inside the building explain and illustrate changes in the Angus countryside in the last 200 years.

Location: OS Ref. NO385 467. Off A94, in Glamis, 5m SW of Forfar.

Opening Times: Good Fri - Easter Mon & 1 May - 30 Sept; daily, 11am - 5pm. Weekends in Oct: 11am - 5pm, last admission 4.30pm.

Admission: Adult £2.50, Conc. £1.70, Family £6.70. Groups: Adult £2, School £1.

House suitable. WC. Limited.

ARBROATH ABBEY

Tel: 01241 878756

Arbroath, Tayside

Owner: Historic Scotland   **Contact:** The Custodian

The substantial ruins of a Tironensian monastery, notably the gate house range and the abbot's house. Arbroath Abbey holds a very special place in Scottish history. It was here in 1320 that Scotland's nobles swore their independence from England in the famous 'Declaration of Arbroath'.

Location: OS Ref. NO644 414. In Arbroath town centre on the A92.

Opening Times: 1 Apr - 30 Sept: daily 9.30am - 6.30pm, last ticket 6pm. 1 Oct - 31 Mar: Mon - Sat, 9.30am - 4.30 pm, Suns, 2 - 4.30pm, last ticket 4pm.

Admission: Adult £1.80, Child 75p, Conc. £1.30.

BALGONIE CASTLE

Tel: 01592 750119   Fax: 01592 753103

Markinch, Fife KY7 6HQ

Owner/Contact: The Laird of Balgonie

14th century tower, additions to the building up to 1702. Still lived in by the family. 14th century chapel.

Location: OS Ref. NO313 006. ¹/₂ m S of A911 Glenrothes - Leven road at Milton of Balgonie on to B921.

Opening Times: All year: daily, 10am - 5pm.

Admission: Adult £3, Child £1.50, OAP £2.

Partially suitable. Obligatory. Strictly no dogs. Resident deerhounds.

BALHOUSIE CASTLE (BLACK WATCH MUSEUM)

Tel: 01738 621281

Hay Street, North Inch Park, Perth PH1 5HR

Owner: MOD   **Contact:** Major McKinnell

Regimental museum housed in the castle.

Location: OS Ref. NO115 244. ¹/₂ m N of town centre, E of A9 road to Dunkeld.

Opening Times: May - Sept: Mon - Sat, 10am - 4.30pm. Oct - Apr: Mon - Fri, 10am - 3.30pm. Closed 23 Dec - 5 Jan & last Sat in Jun.

Admission: Free.

Not suitable. By arrangement. Limited. Guide dogs only.

Balhousie Castle (Black Watch Museum), Perthshire.

BARRIE'S BIRTHPLACE

Tel: 01575 572646   Fax: 01307 840233

9 Brechin Road, Kirriemuir, Angus DD8 4BX

Owner: The National Trust for Scotland   **Contact:** Karen Gilmour or Mrs Sheila Philip

'Do you believe in fairies?' The creator of the eternal magic of *Peter Pan*, J M Barrie, was born here in 1860. He was the ninth of ten children born to David Barrie, a handloom weaver and his wife Margaret Ogilvy. See the imaginative exhibition about this famous novelist and dramatist with life-size figures, miniature stage sets, dioramas, theatre posters and stage costumes, while a darting light, 'Tinkerbell', moves around the room!

Location: OS Ref. NO388 542. On A926/B957, in Kirriemuir, 6m NW of Forfar.

Opening Times: Good Fri - Easter Mon & 1 May - 3 Oct: Mon - Sat, 11am - 5.30pm, Suns, 1.30 - 5.30pm. Weekends in Oct: Sats, 11am - 5.30pm, Suns, 1.30pm - 5.30pm, last adm. 5pm.

Admission: Adult £2, Child £1.30, Family £5.30. Groups: Adult £1.60, School £1.

Stairlift. No parking.

BARRY MILL

Tel: 01241 856761

Barry, Carnoustie, Angus DD7 7RJ

Owner: The National Trust for Scotland   **Contact:** Peter Ellis

19th century meal mill. Demonstrations and displays. Waymarked walks. Picnic area.

Location: OS Ref. NO533 349. N of village between A92 & A930, 2m W of Carnoustie.

Opening Times: Good Fri - Easter Mon & 1 May - 3 Oct; daily, 11am - 5pm. Weekends in Oct: 11am - 5pm.

Admission: Adult £2, Child £1.30, Family £5.30. Groups: Adult £1.60, School £1.

BLAIR CASTLE

See page 50 for full page entry.

BOLFRACKS GARDEN

Tel: 01887 820207

Aberfeldy, Perthshire PH15 2EX

Owner/Contact: Mr J D Hutchison

A garden of approximately 4 acres with splendid views over the River Tay to the hills beyond. A walled garden contains a wide collection of trees, shrubs and perennials. Also a burn garden with rhododendrons, azaleas, meconopsis, primulas etc. with peat wall arrangements. Lots of bulbs and good autumn colour.

Location: OS Ref. NN822 481. 2m W of Aberfeldy on A827 towards Kenmore.

Opening Times: 1 Apr - 31 Oct: daily, 10am - 6pm.

Admission: Adult £2.50, Child (under 16 yrs) Free.

BRANKLYN GARDEN

Tel: 01738 625535

Dundee Road, Perth PH2 7BB

Owner: The National Trust for Scotland   **Contact:** Steve McNamara

Small but magnificent garden with an impressive collection of rare and unusual plants. Among the most breathtaking is the Himalayan blue poppy, *Meconopsis x sheldonii*. There is a rock garden with purple maple and the rare golden *Cedrus*. Seasonal highlights in May and June are the alpines and rhododendrons and in autumn the fiery red *Acer palmatum*.

Location: OS Ref. NO125 225. On A85 at 116 Dundee Road, Perth.

Opening Times: 1 Mar - 31 Oct; daily, 9.30am - sunset.

Admission: Adult £2.50, Conc. £1.70, Family £6.70. Groups: Adult £2, School £1.

Grounds suitable, but limited access.

CAMBO GARDENS

Tel: 01333 450054   Fax: 01333 450987

Cambo Estate, Kingsbarns, St Andrews, Fife KY16 8QD

Owner: Mr & Mrs T P N Erskine   **Contact:** Catherine Erskine

Enchanting Victorian walled garden designed around the Cambo Burn. Snowdrops, lilac and roses are specialities. Ornamental potager, autumn borders. Garden supplies mansion house (not open) with fruit, vegetables and flowers. Woodland walks to sandy beach.

Location: OS Ref. NO603 114. 3m N of Crail. 7m SE of St Andrews on A917.

Opening Times: All year: daily except Christmas and New Year, 10am - dusk.

Admission: Adult £2, Child Free.

Conferences. Limited for coaches. In grounds, on leads. 2 doubles & self-catering apartment.

CASTLE MENZIES

Tel: 01887 820982

Weem, Aberfeldy, Perth PH15 2JD

Owner: Menzies Charitable Trust   **Contact:** R A Adam

Magnificent example of a 16th century 'Z' plan fortified tower house, seat of the Chiefs of Clan Menzies for over 400 years. 'Bonnie Prince Charlie' was given hospitality here in 1746. Visitors can explore the whole building, together with part of 19th century addition. Small clan museum and gift shop.

Location: OS Ref. NN838 497. 1¹/₂ m from Aberfeldy on B846.

Opening Times: 1 Apr - 16 Oct: Mon - Sat, 10.30am - 5pm, Suns, 2 - 5pm, last entry 4.30pm.

Admission: Adult £3, Child £1.50, Conc. £2.50, Groups (20+): Adult £2.70.

Ground floor suitable. WC. Guide dogs only.

CHARLETON HOUSE

Tel: 01333 340249 **Fax:** 01333 340583

Colinsburgh, Leven, Fife KY9 1HG
Location: OS Ref. NO464 036. Off A917. 1m NW of Colinsburgh. 3m NW of Elie.
Opening Times: Sept: 12 - 3pm. Admission every ¹/₂ hr with guided tours only.
Admission: £6.

 Obligatory.

CLUNY HOUSE GARDENS

Tel: 01887 820795

Aberfeldy, Perthshire PH15 2JT   **Contact:** W Mattingley
Good woodland garden including many rare Himalayan species.
Location: OS Ref. NN879 513. 3¹/₂ m NW of Aberfeldy on the Weem to Strathtay Road.
Opening Times: 1 Mar - 31 Oct: 10am - 6pm.
Admission: Adult £2.50, Child under 16 free, Groups: £2 per person (guided tour).

 Not suitable.   By arrangement.   Limited.

CULROSS PALACE

Tel: 01383 880359 **Fax:** 01383 882675

Culross, Fife KY12 8JH
Owner: The National Trust for Scotland   **Contact:** Michael Ford
Relive the domestic life of the 16th and 17th centuries at this Royal Burgh fringed by the River Forth. Here the old buildings and cobbled streets create a time warp for visitors as they explore the old town. Enjoy too the Palace, dating from 1597 and the medieval garden.
Location: OS Ref. NS985 860. Off A985. 12m W of Forth Road Bridge and 4m E of Kincardine Bridge, Fife.
Opening Times: Palace: 1 Apr - 30 Sept: daily, 11am - 5pm, last admission 4pm. Town house & study: same dates, 1.30 - 5pm and weekends in Oct: 11am - 5pm. Groups other times by appointment. Tearoom (in Bessie Bar Hall) dates as Town house, 10.30am - 4.30pm.
Admission: Adult £4.40, Conc. £2.90, Family £11.70. Groups: Adult £3.50, School £1.

WC.   By arrangement.   P

DUNFERMLINE ABBEY & PALACE

Tel: 01383 739026

Dunfermline, Fife
Owner: Historic Scotland   **Contact:** The Custodian
The remains of the Benedictine abbey founded by Queen Margaret in the 11th century. The foundations of her church are under the 12th century Romanesque-style nave. Robert the Bruce was buried in the choir. Substantial parts of the Abbey buildings remain, including the vast refectory.
Location: OS Ref. NY090 873. In Dunfermline off the M90.
Opening Times: 1 Apr - 30 Sept: daily, 9.30am - 6.30pm, last ticket 6pm. 1 Oct - 31 Mar: Mon - Sat, 9.30am - 4.30pm, Suns, 2 - 4.30pm, last ticket 4pm. Closed Thur pm and Fris in winter.
Admission: Adult £1.80, Child 75p, Conc. £1.30.

EDZELL CASTLE AND GARDEN

Tel: 01356 648631

Edzell, Angus
Owner: Historic Scotland   **Contact:** The Custodian
The beautiful walled garden at Edzell is one of Scotland's unique sights, created by Sir David Lindsay in 1604. The 'Pleasance' is a delightful formal garden with walls decorated with sculptured stone panels, flower boxes and niches for nesting birds. The fine tower house, now ruined, dates from the last years of the 15th century. Mary Queen of Scots held a council meeting in the castle in 1562 on her way north as her army marched against the Gordons.
Location: OS Ref. NO585 691. At Edzell, 6m N of Brechin on B966. 1m W of village.
Opening Times: 1 Apr - 30 Sept: daily, 9.30am - 6.30pm, last ticket 6pm. 1 Oct - 31 Mar: Mon - Sat, 9.30am - 4.30pm, Suns, 2 - 4.30pm, last ticket 4pm. Closed Thur pm and Fris in winter.
Admission: Adult £2.50, Child £1, Conc. £1.90.

ELCHO CASTLE

Tel: 0131 668 8800

Perth
Owner: Historic Scotland
This handsome and complete fortified mansion of 16th century date has four projecting towers. The original wrought-iron grilles to protect the windows are still in place.
Location: OS Ref. NO164 211. On the Tay, 3m SE of Perth.
Opening Times: Tel: 0131 668 8800 for details.
Admission: Adult £1.80, Child 75p, Conc. £1.30.

DRUMMOND CASTLE GARDENS

Kathy Collins

MUTHILL, CRIEFF, PERTHSHIRE PH5 2AA
Owner: Grimsthorpe & Drummond Castle Trust   **Contact:** *Joe Buchanan*

Tel: 01764 681257 **Fax:** 01764 681550

Scotland's most important formal gardens, among the finest in Europe. A mile of beech-lined avenue leads to a formidable ridge top tower house. Enter through the woven iron yett to the terraces and suddenly revealed is a magnificent Italianate parterre, celebrating the saltire and family heraldry, surrounding the famous multiplex sundial by John Milne, master mason to Charles I. First laid out in the early 17th century by John Drummond, the 2nd Earl of Perth and renewed in the early 1950s by Phyllis Astor, Countess of Ancaster.

Location: OS Ref. NN844 181. 2m S of Crieff off the A822.
Opening Times: Easter, then 1 May - 31 Oct: 2 - 6pm, last entry 5pm.
Admission: Adult £3, Child £1.50, OAP £2.

Partially suitable.   P   In grounds, on leads.

SPECIAL EVENTS
AUG 1: Open Day, 2 - 5pm, entertainments, teas, raffle.

Perthshire
Scotland

FALKLAND PALACE

FALKLAND KY15 7BU

Owner: *The National Trust for Scotland*   **Contact:** *Mrs Margaret Marshall*

Tel: 01337 857397   **Fax:** 01337 857980

The Royal Palace of Falkland, set in the heart of a unique medieval village, was the country residence and hunting lodge of eight Stuart monarchs, including Mary Queen of Scots. Built between 1502 and 1541, the Palace is an extremely fine example of Renaissance architecture. It includes the exceptionally beautiful Chapel Royal, and is surrounded by internationally known gardens, laid out in the 1950s. The Royal Tennis Court, reputedly the world's oldest, is still used today.

Location: OS Ref. NO253 075. A912, 11m N of Kirkcaldy.

Opening Times: Palace & Garden: 1 Apr - 31 Oct: Mon - Sat, 11am - 5.30pm, Suns, 1.30 - 5.30pm, last admission to Palace 4.30pm, to Garden 5pm. Groups at other times by appointment. Town Hall by appointment only.

Admission: Adult £5, Conc. £3.40, Family £13.50. Groups: Adult £4, School £1. Garden only: Adult £2.50, Conc. £1.70. Groups: Adult £2, School £1.

Grounds suitable.

HOUSE OF DUN

MONTROSE, ANGUS DD10 9LQ

Owner: *The National Trust for Scotland*   **Contact:** *John Oatts*

Tel: 01674 810264   **Fax:** 01674 810722

This beautiful Georgian house, overlooking the Montrose Basin, was designed by William Adam and built in 1730 for David Erskine, Lord Dun. Lady Augusta Kennedy-Erskine was the natural daughter of William IV and Mrs Jordan and House of Dun contains many royal mementos. The house features superb plasterwork by Joseph Enzer.

Location: OS Ref. NO670 599. 3m W Montrose on A935.

Opening Times: House & shop: Good Fri - Easter Mon & 1 May - 3 Oct: daily, 1.30 - 5.30pm. Weekends in Oct: 1.30 - 5.30pm, last admission 5pm. Restaurant: same dates but opens 11am. Garden & grounds: all year, daily 9.30am - sunset.

Admission: Adult £3.90, Conc. £2.60, Family £10.40. Groups: Adult £3.20, School £1. Gardens & grounds: Honesty box £1.

Conferences.   Ground floor & basement suitable. WC.   In grounds, on leads. Special dog walk.

GLAMIS CASTLE

See page 51 for full page entry.

GLENEAGLES

Tel: 01764 682388

Auchterarder, Perthshire PH3 1PJ

Owner: Gleneagles 1996 Trust   **Contact:** J Martin Haldane of Gleneagles

Gleneagles has been the home of the Haldane family since the 12th century. The 18th century pavilion is open to the public by written appointment.

Location: OS Ref. NS931 088. Auchterarder.

Opening Times: By written appointment only.

HILL OF TARVIT MANSIONHOUSE

Tel/Fax: 01334 653127

Cupar, Fife KY15 5PB

Owner: The National Trust for Scotland   **Contact:** Mrs June Pratt

This fine house was rebuilt in 1906 by Sir Robert Lorimer, the renowned Scottish architect, for a Dundee industrialist, Mr F B Sharp. The house still presents a perfect setting for Mr Sharp's notable collection of superb French, Chippendale and vernacular furniture. Fine paintings by Raeburn and Ramsay and a number of eminent Dutch artists are on view together with Chinese porcelain and bronzes. Don't miss the restored Edwardian laundry behind the house which is set in the midst of a delightful garden.

Location: OS Ref. NO379 118. Off A916, 2½m S of Cupar, Fife.

Opening Times: House: Good Fri - Easter Mon & 1 May - 3 Oct: daily, 1.30 - 5.30pm. Weekends in Oct: 1.30 - 5.30pm, last admission 4.45pm. Tearoom: same dates but opens 12.30pm. Garden & Grounds: 1 Apr - 31 Oct: daily, 9.30am - 9pm; 1 Nov - 31 Mar: daily, 9.30am - 4.30pm.

Admission: Adult £3.90, Conc. £2.60, Family £10.40. Groups: Adult £3.20, School £1.

Ground floor & grounds suitable. WC.   By arrangement.   P

HOUSE OF PITMUIES

Tel/Fax: 01241 828245

Guthrie by Forfar, Angus DD8 2SD

Owner/Contact: Mrs Farquhar Ogilive

Semi-formal walled gardens celebrated for their delphiniums, rose collection and herbaceous borders in summer. Cool woodland and riverside walks with fine trees and massed spring bulbs. Fine 18th century house (open by appointment) flanked by stone-roofed outbuildings with adjacent 'gothick' wash house and unique turreted doo-cot.

Location: OS Ref. NO567 500. A932, 6½m E of Forfar, 8m NW of Arbroath, 1½m W of Friockheim.

Opening Times: Garden only: Easter - 31 Oct: daily, 10am - 5pm. House by appointment.

Admission: Garden: Adult £2, Child (under 12) Free.

For pre-booked groups.   P Free.   In grounds, on leads.

HUNTINGTOWER CASTLE

Tel: 01738 627231

Perth

Owner: Historic Scotland   **Contact:** The Custodian

The splendid painted ceilings are especially noteworthy in this castle, once owned by the Ruthven family. Scene of a famous leap between two towers by a daughter of the house who was nearly caught in her lover's room. The two towers are still complete, one of 15th - 16th century date, the other of 16th century origin. Now linked by a 17th century range.

Location: OS Ref. NO084 252. 3m NW of Perth off the A85.

Opening Times: 1 Apr - 30 Sept: daily, 9.30am - 6.30pm, last ticket 6pm. 1 Oct - 31 Mar: Mon - Sat, 9.30am - 4.30pm, Suns, 2 - 4.30pm, last ticket 4pm. Closed Thur pm & Fris in winter.

Admission: Adult £1.80, Child 75p, Conc. £1.30.

INCHCOLM ABBEY

Tel: 01383 823332

Inchcolm, Fife

Owner: Historic Scotland   **Contact:** The Custodian

Known as the 'Iona of the East'. This is the best preserved group of monastic buildings in Scotland, founded in 1123. Includes a 13th century octagonal chapter house.

Location: OS Ref. NT190 826. On Inchcolm in the Firth of Forth. Reached by ferry from South Queensferry (30 mins) tel. 0131 331 4857, and from North Queensferry (weather permitting).

Opening Times: 1 Apr - 30 Sept: daily, 9.30am - 6.30pm, last ticket 6pm.

Admission: Adult £2.50, Child £1, Conc. £1.90. Additional charge for ferries.

Perthshire Scotland

INCHMAHOME PRIORY

Tel: 01877 385294

Port of Menteith

Owner: Historic Scotland   **Contact:** The Custodian

A beautifully situated Augustinian priory on an island in the Lake of Menteith founded in 1238 with much of the building surviving. The five year old Mary Queen of Scots was sent here for safety in 1547.

Location: OS Ref. NN574 005. On an island in Lake of Menteith. Reached by ferry from Port of Menteith, 4m E of Aberfoyle off A81.

Opening Times: 1 Apr - 30 Sept: daily, 9.30am - 6.30pm, last ticket 6pm.

Admission: Adult £3, Child £1, Conc. £2.30. Charge includes ferry trip.

Edzell Castle & Garden, Perthshire.

LOCH LEVEN CASTLE

Tel: 01786 450000

Loch Leven, Kinross

Owner: Historic Scotland   **Contact:** The Regional Custodian

Mary Queen of Scots endured nearly a year of imprisonment in this 14th century tower before her dramatic escape in May 1568. During the First War of Independence it was held by the English, stormed by Wallace and visited by Bruce.

Location: OS Ref. NO138 018. On island in Loch Leven reached by ferry from Kinross off the M90.

Opening Times: 1 Apr - 30 Sept: daily, 9.30am - 6.30pm, last ticket 6pm.

Admission: Adult £3, Child £1, Conc. £2.30. Prices include ferry trip.

MEGGINCH CASTLE GARDENS

Tel: 01821 642222 **Fax:** 01821 642708

Errol, Perthshire PH2 7SW

Owner: Captain Drummond of Megginch and Lady Strange

15th century castle, 1,000 year old yews, flowered parterre, double walled kitchen garden, topiary, astrological garden, pagoda dovecote in courtyard. Part used as a location for the film *Rob Roy*.

Location: OS Ref. NO241 245. 8m E of Perth on A90.

Opening Times: Apr - Oct: Weds. Aug: daily, 2.30 - 6pm.

Admission: Adult £2.50, Child £1.

⊤ &Partially suitable. By arrangement. P Limited for coaches. In grounds, on leads.

MEIGLE SCULPTURED STONE MUSEUM

Tel: 01828 640612

Meigle

Owner: Historic Scotland

A remarkable collection of 25 sculptured monuments of the Celtic Christian period. This is one of the finest collections of Dark Age sculpture in Western Europe.

Location: OS Ref. NO287 446. In Meigle on the A94.

Opening Times: 1 Apr - 30 Sept: daily, 9.30am - 6.30pm, last ticket 6pm.

Admission: Adult £1.80, Child 75p, Conc. £1.30.

MONZIE CASTLE

Tel: 01764 653110

Crieff, Perthshire PH7 4HD

Owner/Contact: Mrs C M M Crichton

Built in 1791. Destroyed by fire in 1908 and rebuilt and furnished by Sir Robert Lorimer.

Location: OS Ref. NN873 244. 2m NE of Crieff.

Opening Times: 15 May - 13 Jun: daily, 2 - 5pm. By appointment at other times.

Admission: Adult £3, Child £1. Groups: Adult £2.50.

PITTENCRIEFF HOUSE

Tel: 01383 313838/722935

Dunfermline, Fife

Owner: Fife Council   **Contact:** Ms Lin Collis

17th century T-plan house now housing a collection of costumes. Displays on the history of the house and park. Art gallery.

Location: OS Ref. NN087 873. In Dunfermline, S of A994 in Pittencrieff Park.

Opening Times: All year. May - Oct: 11am - 5pm. Nov - Apr: 11am - 4pm.

Admission: Free.

KELLIE CASTLE & GARDEN

PITTENWEEM, FIFE KY10 2RF

Owner: The National Trust for Scotland   *Contact: The Property Manager*

Tel: 01333 720271 **Fax:** 01333 720326

This very fine example of domestic architecture in Lowland Scotland dates from the 14th century and was sympathetically restored by the Lorimer family in the late 19th century. The castle contains magnificent plaster ceilings and painted panelling as well as fine furniture designed by Sir Robert Lorimer. Of particular interest are the Victorian nursery and the old kitchen. The late Victorian garden features a fine collection of old-fashioned roses and herbaceous plants which are cultivated organically.

Location: OS Ref. NO519 051. On B9171, 3m NW of Pittenweem, Fife.

Opening Times: Castle: Good Fri - Easter Mon & 1 May - 3 Oct: daily, 1.30 - 5.30pm. Weekends in Oct: 1.30 - 5.30pm, last admission 4.45pm. Garden & grounds: All year, daily, 9.30am - sunset.

Admission: Adult £3.90, Conc. £2.60, Family £10.40. Groups: Adult £3.20, School £1.

 Ground floor & grounds suitable.

Inchmahome Priory, Perthshire.

ST ANDREWS CASTLE

THE SCORES, ST ANDREWS, KY16 9AR

Owner: *Historic Scotland* **Contact:** *The Steward*

Tel: 01334 477196

This was the castle of the Bishops of St Andrews and has a fascinating mine and counter-mine, rare examples of medieval siege techniques. There is also a bottle dungeon hollowed out of solid rock. Cardinal Beaton was murdered here and John Knox was sent to the galleys when the ensuing siege was lifted.

Location: OS Ref. NO513 169. In St Andrews on the A91.

Opening Times: Apr - Sept: daily, 9.30am - 6.30pm. Oct - Mar: Mon - Sat, 9.30am - 4.30pm; Suns, 2 - 4.30pm. Last ticket 30 mins before closing. Joint ticket with St Andrews Cathedral available.

Admission: Adult £2.50, Child £1, OAP/Student £1.90. 10% discount for groups (10+). Free pre-booked school visits.

⚹ Visitor centre. ⚹ ⚹ Private evening hire. ⚹ Partially suitable. WCs.
⚹ By arrangement. ⚹ On street. ⚹ Free if booked. ⚹ Guide dogs only.

ST ANDREWS CATHEDRAL   **Tel:** 01334 472563

St Andrews, Fife

Owner: Historic Scotland **Contact:** The Administrator

The remains still give a vivid impression of the scale of what was once the largest cathedral in Scotland along with the associated domestic ranges of the priory. The precinct walls are particularly well preserved. Climb St Rule's Tower for a magnificent view of the town and visit the cathedral's collection of celtic and medieval carved stones and other relics found on the site.

Location: OS Ref: NO514 167. In St Andrews.

Opening Times: 1 Apr - 30 Sept: daily, 9.30am - 6.30pm, last ticket 6pm. 1 Oct - 31 Mar: Mon - Sat, 9.30am - 4.30pm, Suns, 2 - 4.30pm, last ticket 4pm.

Admission: Adult £1.80, Child 75p, Conc. £1.30. Joint entry ticket available with St Andrews Castle: Adult £3.50, Conc. £2.70, Child £1.25.

SCONE PALACE   *See page 52 for full page entry.*

SCOTLAND'S SECRET BUNKER   **Tel:** 01333 310301 **Fax:** 01333 312040

Troywood, St Andrews KY16 8QH **Contact:** General Manager

100ft underground is the secret bunker where the Government would have gone in the event of a nuclear war. Operations room. Cinemas. Restaurants. A unique family day out.

Location: OS Ref. NO562 090. Off the B940, 6m S of St Andrews. Thistle signs.

Opening Times: Please telephone for details.

Admission: Adult £5.95, Child £3.25, Conc. £4.95, Family £16. Curator's tours by arrangement. (1998 prices).

STOBHALL GARDENS & CHAPEL   **Tel:** 01821 640332

Stobhall, Guildtown, Perthshire PH2 6DR

Owner: The Earl of Perth **Contact:** J Stormonth-Darling

Dramatic shrub gardens surround this unusual and charming cluster of historic buildings in a magnificent situation overlooking the River Tay. Access to 14th century chapel with its unique painted ceiling (1630).

Location: OS Ref. NO132 343. 8m N of Perth on A93.

Opening Times: 22 May - 19 Jun: 1 - 5pm. Also 24 & 31 October: 2 - 5pm.

Admission: Adult £2, Child £1.

⚹ Partially suitable. WC. ⚹ Limited. ⚹ ⚹ Guide dogs only.

St Andrews Castle, Fife.

West Highlands,
Loch Lomond & Stirling

Killin Falls of Dochart. Argyll, the Isles, Loch Lomond, Stirling & Trossachs Tourist Board

ARGYLL'S LODGING
Stirling

Owner: Historic Scotland

CONTACT

Jon MacNeil
Argyll's Lodging
Castle Wynd
Stirling
FK8 1EJ

Tel: 01786 431323

Fax: 01786 448194

ARGYLL'S LODGING, the residence of the Earls of Argyll in Stirling, is the finest and most complete surviving example in Scotland of a 17th century town residence. Set back behind a screen wall on the upper approaches to Stirling Castle, its fine architecture marks it out as a town house intended for the household of a great nobleman serving the Royal Stewart Court within the Castle. The principal rooms within the lodging – including the Laigh Hall, Dining Room, Drawing Room and Bedchamber – have recently been restored and furnished as they would have been when the 9th Earl of Argyll lived there in 1680. The Earl was executed for treason in 1685.

OPENING TIMES

April - September:
Daily: 9.30am - 6pm.

October - March:
Daily: 9.30am - 5pm.

LOCATION

OS Ref. NS793 938

At the top and on E side of Castle Wynd in Stirling.

Train: Stirling.

Air: Edinburgh or Glasgow.

ADMISSION

Adult £2.80
Child* £1.20
Conc.......................£2.00

*up to 16 years

FUNCTION

ROOM	SIZE	MAX CAPACITY
Laigh Hall	11 x 6m	60 for reception
High Dining Room	11 x 6m	26 for dinner
Both rooms: 120 for receptions		

Interpretation scheme includes computer animations; joint ticket with Stirling Castle available.

Evening receptions/dinners.

Partially suitable. No wheelchair access to upper floor.

Ample parking for coaches and cars on Stirling Castle Esplanade.

Free pre-booked school visits scheme.

Guide dogs only.

INVERARAY CASTLE
Inveraray

The Duke of Argyll's family have lived in Inveraray since the early 15th century. The present Castle was built between 1740 and 1790.

The ancient Royal Burgh of Inveraray lies about 60 miles north west of Glasgow by Loch Fyne in an area of spectacular natural beauty combining the ruggedness of highland scenery with the sheltered tidal loch 90 miles from the open sea.

The Castle is the home of the Duke and Duchess of Argyll. Its fairytale exterior belies the grandeur of its gracious interior. The building was designed by Roger Morris and decorated by Robert Mylne, the clerk of works being William Adam, father of Robert and John, who did much of the laying out of the present Royal Burgh, an unrivalled example of an early planned town.

Visitors may see the famous Armoury Hall containing some 1300 pieces, French tapestries made especially for the Castle, fine examples of Scottish, English and French furniture together with a wealth of other works of art including china, silver and family artifacts, all of which form a unique collection spanning the generations which are identified by a magnificent genealogical display in the Clan Room.

Owner: Trustees of the 10th Duke of Argyll

CONTACT

The Factor
Dept HHD
Argyll Estates Office
Cherry Park
Inveraray
Argyll
PA32 8XE

Tel: 01499 302203

Fax: 01499 302421

LOCATION

OS Ref. NN100 090

From Edinburgh
2¹/₂ - 3 hrs via Glasgow.

Just NE of Inveraray
on A83. W shore
of Loch Fyne.

Bus: Bus route stopping
point within ¹/₂ m.

OPENING TIMES

3 April - 10 October

April, May, June,
September & October:
Mon -Thur & Sat:
10am - 1pm & 2 - 5.45pm
Fri: Closed
Sun: 1 - 5.45pm.

July & August
Daily: 10am - 5.45pm
(including Friday)
Sun: 1 - 5.45pm.

Last admissions
12.30 & 5pm.

WINTER

Closed.

ADMISSION

House only

Adult £4.50
Child (under 16yrs)...£2.50
OAP/Student..........£3.50
Family (2+2)..........£12.00
Groups (20+)
.... 20% discount

No photography. Guide books in French, Italian, Japanese and German translations.

Visitors may alight at the entrance. Wheelchair ramp to castle plus two steps. All main public rooms suitable but two long flights of stairs to the smaller rooms upstairs. WCs.

Seats up to 50. Menus available on request. Groups book in advance. Tel: 01786 813317.

Available for up to 100 people at no additional cost. Groups please book. Tour time: 1 hr.

100 cars. Separate coach park close to Castle

£1.50 per child. A guide can be provided. Areas of interest include a nature walk.

Guide dogs only.

ACHAMORE GARDENS
Tel: 01583 505254/505267

Isle of Gigha, Argyll PA41 7AD

Owner: Mr and Mrs Derek Holt **Contact:** Mr William Howden

Gardens only open. Sub-tropical gardens created by Sir James Horlick who bought Gigha in 1944.

Location: OS Ref. NR650 500. Off the Mull of Kintyre. Ferry from Tayinloan.

Opening Times: Dawn until dusk every day.

Admission: Adult £2, Child £1.

Grounds suitable.   P   In grounds, on leads.
4 twin, 5 double, all ensuite.

ANGUS'S GARDEN
Tel: 01866 822381 **Fax:** 01866 822652

Barguillean, Taynuilt, Argyll, West Highlands PA35 1HY

Owner: Mr Sam MacDonald **Contact:** Mr Sam MacDonald

Garden of peace, tranquillity and reconciliation.

Location: OS Ref. NM999 298.

Opening Times: All year: daily, 9am - 5pm.

Admission: £2.

ARDENCRAIG GARDENS
Tel/Fax: 01700 504225

Ardencraig, Rothesay, Isle of Bute, West Highlands PA20 9BP

Owner: Argyll and Bute Council **Contact:** Martin Deighan

Walled garden, greenhouses.

Location: OS Ref. NS105 645. 2m from Rothesay.

Opening Times: May - Sept: Mon - Fri, 10am - 4.30pm, Sat and Sun, 1 - 4.30pm.

Admission: Free.

ARDUAINE GARDEN

Harvey Wood

ARDUAINE, BY OBAN, ARGYLL PA34 4XQ

Owner: The National Trust for Scotland *Contact:* Maurice Wilkins

Tel/Fax: 01852 200366

A haven of tranquillity nestling on the west coast, Arduaine Garden is most spectacular in the late spring and early summer when the rhododendrons and azaleas are at their glorious best. With informal perennial borders giving a delightful display of colour throughout the season, the garden offers pleasant surroundings for a relaxing walk through the woodland garden to the coastal viewpoint, or simply an opportunity to sit and enjoy the peaceful atmosphere of the water garden.

Location: OS Ref. NM798 105. On A816, 20m S of Oban and 17m N of Lochgilphead.

Opening Times: All year: daily, 9.30am - sunset.

Admission: Adult £2.50, Conc. £1.70, Family £6.70. Groups: Adult £2. School £1.

By arrangement.   P   Guide dogs only.

ARGYLL'S LODGING   See page 60 for full page entry.

AUCHINDRAIN TOWNSHIP
Tel: 01499 500235

Auchindrain, Inveraray, Argyll PA32 8XN

Owner: Auchindrain Trust **Contact:** John McDonald

Open-air museum of an original West Highland township with restored buildings to give a fascinating experience of what life was really like for the Highlander in past centuries.

Location: OS Ref. NN050 050. On A83, 6m SW of Inveraray.

Opening Times: Apr - Sept: daily, 10am - 5pm.

Admission: Adult £3, Child £1.50, OAP £2.50.

P   In grounds, on leads.

BALLOCH CASTLE COUNTRY PARK
Tel: 01389 758216 **Fax:** 01389 755721

Balloch, Dunbartonshire G83 8LX

Contact: Loch Lomond Park Authority Ranger Service

A 200 acre country park on the banks of Loch Lomond. This ancient seat of the Lennox offers the visitor a chance to blend the wild, natural beauty of Scotland with the formal glory of the ornamental gardens and splendid trees of former estate days. Balloch Castle, now the Visitor Centre, was built in 1808 in the 'castle-gothic' style.

Location: OS Ref. NS390 830. SE shore of Loch Lomond, off A82 for Balloch or A811 for Stirling.

Opening Times: Visitor Centre: Easter - Oct: daily, 10am - 5.30pm. Country Park: All year, dawn - dusk.

Admission: Free for both Visitor Centre and Country Park.

Visitor Centre.   Partially suitable. WCs.   P Limited for coaches.
In grounds, on leads.

BANNOCKBURN HERITAGE CENTRE
Tel: 01786 812664 **Fax:** 01786 810892

Glasgow Road, Stirling FK7 0LJ

Owner: The National Trust for Scotland **Contact:** Judith Fairley

In 1314 from this battlefield the Scots 'sent them homeward to think again', when Edward II's English army was soundly defeated by King Robert the Bruce. Inside the Heritage Centre there is a life-size statue of William Wallace, Bruce on his throne, a display enriched with replicas, vignettes of Scottish life and a panorama of historical characters.

Location: OS Ref. NS810 910. Off M80 & M9/J9, 2m S of Stirling.

Opening Times: Site: All year: daily. Heritage Centre shop: 1 - 31 Mar and 1 Nov - 23 Dec: daily, 11am - 3pm. 1 Apr - 31 Oct: daily, 10am - 5.30pm (last visual show ¹/₂ hr before closing).

Admission: Adult £2.50, Conc. £1.70, Family £6.70. Groups: Adult £2, School £1.

P   In grounds, on leads.

BONAWE IRON FURNACE
Tel: 01866 822432

Taynuilt, Argyll

Owner: Historic Scotland **Contact:** The Custodian

Founded in 1753 by Cumbrian iron masters this is the most complete remaining charcoal fuelled ironworks in Britain. Displays show how iron was once made here.

Location: OS Ref. NN005 310. By the village of Taynuilt off the A85.

Opening Times: 1 Apr - 30 Sept: daily, 9.30am - 6.30pm, last ticket 6pm.

Admission: Adult £2.50, Child £1, Conc. £1.90.

CASTLE CAMPBELL
Tel: 01259 742408

Dollar Glen, Central District

Owner: The National Trust for Scotland **Contact:** Historic Scotland

Known as 'Castle Gloom' this spectacularly sited 15th century fortress was the lowland stronghold of the Campbells. Stunning views from the parapet walk.

Location: OS Ref. NS961 993. At head of Dollar Glen, 10m E of Stirling on the A91.

Opening Times: 1 Apr - 30 Sept: daily, 9.30am - 6.30pm, last ticket 6pm. 1 Oct - 31 Mar: Mon - Sat, 9.30am - 4.30pm (closed Thur pm & Fri all day) Suns, 2 - 4.30pm, last ticket 4pm.

Admission: Adult £2.50, Child £1, Conc. £1.90.

CASTLE STALKER
Tel: 01883 622768 **Fax:** 01883 626238

Portnacroish, Appin, Argyll PA38 4BA

Owner: Mrs M Allward **Contact:** Messrs R & A Allward

Early 15th century tower house and ancient seat of the Stewarts of Appin. Picturesquely set on a rocky islet approx 400 yds off the mainland on the shore of Loch Linnhe. Reputed to have been used by James IV as a hunting lodge. Garrisoned by Government troops during the 1745 rising. Restored from a ruin by the late Lt Col Stewart Allward following acquisition in 1965 and now retained by his family.

Location: OS Ref. NM930 480. Approx. 20m N of Oban on the A828. On islet ¹/₄ m off-shore.

Opening Times: Apr - Sept for 25 days. Telephone for details. Times variable depending on tides and weather.

Admission: Adult £6, Child £3.

Not suitable for coach parties.   Not suitable.

W.Highlands/Stirling Scotland

DOUNE CASTLE
Tel: 01786 841742

Doune

Owner: Earl of Moray (leased to Historic Scotland)   **Contact:** The Custodian

A formidable 14th century courtyard castle, built for the Regent Albany. The striking keep-gatehouse combines domestic quarters including the splendid Lord's Hall with its carved oak screen, musicians' gallery and double fireplace.

Location: OS Ref. NN720 020. In Doune, 8m S of Callendar on the A84.

Opening Times: 1 Apr - 30 Sept: daily, 9.30am - 6.30pm. 1 Oct - 31 Mar: Mon - Wed & Sat, 9.30am - 4.30pm, Thur, 9.30am - 12 noon, Fris, closed, Suns, 2 - 4.30pm, last admission 1/2 hr before closing.

Admission: Adult £2.30, Child £1, Conc. £1.75.

DUART CASTLE

ISLE OF MULL, ARGYLL PA64 6AP
Owner/Contact: Sir Lachlan Maclean Bt

Tel: 01680 812309 or 01577 830311

Duart Castle has been a Maclean stronghold since the 12th century. The keep was built by Lachlan Lubanach, 5th Chief, in 1360. Burnt by the English in 1758, the castle was restored in 1912 and today is still the home of the Chief of the Clan Maclean. It has a spectacular position overlooking the Sound of Mull.

Location: OS Ref. NM750 350. Off A849 on the east point of the Isle of Mull.

Opening Times: 1 May - 11 Oct: 10.30am - 6pm.

Admission: Adult £3.50, Child £1.75, Conc. £3, Family £8.75.

DUNSTAFFNAGE CASTLE

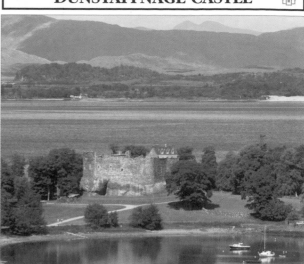

BY OBAN, ARGYLL PA37 1PZ
Owner: Historic Scotland   Contact: The Steward

Tel: 01631 562465

A very fine 13th century castle built on a rock with a great curtain wall. The castle's colourful history stretches across the Wars of Independence to the 1745 rising. The castle was briefly the prison of Flora Macdonald. Marvellous views from the top of the curtain wall. Close by are the remains of a chapel with beautiful architectural detail.

Location: OS49 NM882 344. By Loch Etive, 3 1/2 m from Oban on the A85.

Opening Times: Apr - Sept: daily, 9.30am - 6.30pm, last ticket 1/2 hr before closing. Oct - Mar: Mon - Sat, 9.30am - 4.30pm; Suns, 2 - 4.30pm.

Admission: Adult £1.80, Child 75p, Conc. £1.30. 10% discount for groups (10+).

Partially suitable. By arrangement. Free pre-booked school visits. In grounds, on leads.

GLENCOE   **Tel:** 01855 811307/811729 (during closed season) **Fax:** 01855 811772

Ballachulish, Argyll PA39 4HX

Owner: The National Trust for Scotland   **Contact:** Derrick Warner

This is a breathtaking, dramatic glen with jagged peaks incised on either side by cascading water. In 1692 many of the MacDonald clan were massacred by soldiers of King William's army, to whom they had given hospitality. Wildlife abounds and herds of red deer, wildcat and golden eagle enjoy this wilderness area.

Location: OS Ref. NN100 590. Off A82, 17m S of Fort William.

Opening Times: Site: All year, daily. Visitor Centre & snack bar: 1 Apr - 18 May and 1 Sept - 31 Oct: daily, 10am - 5pm. 19 May - 31 Aug: daily, 9.30am - 5.30pm, last admission 1/2 hr before closing.

Admission: Adult 50p, Child 30p.

Ground floor suitable. WC. Guide dogs only.

DUMBARTON CASTLE
Tel: 01389 732167

Dumbarton, Strathclyde

Owner: Historic Scotland   **Contact:** The Custodian

Location: OS Ref. NS401 744. In Dumbarton on the A82.

Opening Times: 1 Apr - 30 Sept: daily, 9.30am - 6.30pm, last ticket 6pm. 1 Oct - 31 Mar: Mon - Wed & Sat, 9.30am - 4.30pm, Thur, 9.30am - 12 noon, Fris closed, Suns, 2 - 4.30pm, last ticket 4pm.

Admission: Adult £1.80, Child 75p, Conc £1.30.

DUNBLANE CATHEDRAL
Tel: 01786 823388

Dunblane

Owner: Historic Scotland   **Contact:** The Custodian

One of Scotland's noblest medieval churches. The lower part of the tower is Romanesque but the larger part of the building is of the 13th century. It was restored in 1889 - 93 by Sir Rowand Anderson.

Location: OS Ref. NN782 015. In Dunblane.

Opening Times: All year.

Admission: Free.

Stirling Castle Heads, West Highlands.

Historic Scotland

THE HILL HOUSE

Tel: 01436 673900 **Fax:** 01436 674685

Upper Colquhoun Street, Helensburgh G84 9AJ

Owner: The National Trust for Scotland   **Contact:** Mrs Anne Ellis

Certainly the finest domestic creation of the famous Scottish architect and artist, Charles Rennie Mackintosh. He set this 20th century masterpiece high on a hillside overlooking the Firth of Clyde. Mackintosh also designed furniture, fittings and decorative schemes to complement the house, and suggested a layout for the garden which has been renovated by the Trust.

Location: OS Ref. NS300 820. Off B832, between A82 & A814, 23m NW of Glasgow.

Opening Times: 1 Apr - 31 Oct: daily, 1.30 - 5.30pm, last admission 5pm. Tearoom: 1.30 - 4.30pm. Increasing visitor numbers are placing great strain on the structure of The Hill House, which may be designed for domestic purposes. Access may be restricted at peak times and at the discretion of the Property Manager.

Admission: Adult £6, Conc. £4, Family £16. Groups must book.

INVERARAY CASTLE

See page 61 for full page entry.

INVERARAY JAIL

Tel: 01499 302381 **Fax:** 01499 302195

Church Square, Inveraray, Argyll PA32 8TX

Owner: Visitor Centres Ltd   **Contact:** J Linley

A living 19th century prison! Uniformed prisoners and warders, life-like figures, imaginative exhibitions, sounds, smells and trials in progress, bring the 1820 courtroom and former county prison back to life. See our latest addition – a comparison of life in prison today.

Location: OS Ref. NN100 090. Church Square, Inveraray, Argyll.

Opening Times: Apr - Oct: 9.30am - 6pm, last adm. 5pm. Nov - Mar: 10am - 5pm, last adm. 4pm.

Admission: Adult £4.50, Child £2.20, OAP £2.85, Family £12.30. Groups: £3.55, OAP £2.35.

KILCHURN CASTLE

Tel: 0131 668 8800

Loch Awe, Dalmally, Argyll

Owner: Historic Scotland   **Contact:** The Custodian

A square tower, built by Sir Colin Campbell of Glenorchy c1550, it was much enlarged in 1693 to give the building, now a ruin, its present picturesque outline. Spectacular views of Loch Awe.

Location: OS Ref. NN133 276. At the NE end of Loch Awe, 2½ m W of Dalmally.

Opening Times: Apr - Sept: 9.30am - 6.30pm.

Admission: Free.

MOUNT STUART HOUSE & GARDENS

ISLE OF BUTE PA20 9LR

Owner: The Mount Stuart Trust   *Contact:* The Administrator

Tel: 01700 503877 **Fax:** 01700 505313 **e-mail:** contactus@mountstuart.com

Spectacular High Victorian Gothic house, ancestral home of the Marquesses of Bute. Splendid interiors, art collection and architectural detail. Set in 300 acres of stunning woodlands, mature Victorian pinetum, arboretum and exotic gardens. Countryside Ranger Service. Scottish Tourism Oscar winner.

Location: OS Ref. NS100 600. 5m S of Rothesay Pierhead, local bus service to house. Frequent ferry service from Wemyss Bay, Renfrewshire & Colintraive, Argyll. 1 hr from Glasgow Airport.

Opening Times: 1 May - 17 Oct: daily (closed Tue & Thur). House: 11am - 4.30pm. Gardens: 10am - 5pm.

Admission: House & Gardens: Adult £6, Child £2.50, Family £15, Season £15. Gardens: Adult £3.50, Child £2, Family £9. Conc. & group rates given. Booked guided tours available.

Picnic area. By arrangement.

ROTHESAY CASTLE

Tel: 01700 502691

Rothesay, Isle of Bute

Owner: Historic Scotland   **Contact:** The Custodian

A favourite residence of the Stuart Kings, this is a wonderful example of a 13th century circular castle of enclosure with 16th century forework containing the Great Hall. Attacked by Vikings in its earlier days.

Location: OS Ref. NS088 646. In Rothesay, Isle of Bute. Ferry from Wemyss Bay on the A78.

Opening Times: 1 Apr - 30 Sept: daily, 9.30am - 6.30pm, last ticket 6pm. 1 Oct - 31 Mar: Mon - Wed & Sat, 9.30am - 4.30pm, Thur 9.30am - 12 noon, Fris closed, Suns, 2 - 4.30pm, last ticket 4pm.

Admission: Adult £1.80, Child 75p, Conc. £1.30.

ST BLANE'S CHURCH

Tel: 0131 668 8800

Kingarth, Isle of Bute

Owner: Historic Scotland

This 12th century Romanesque chapel stands on the site of a 12th century Celtic monastery.

Location: OS Ref. NS090 570. At the S end of the Isle of Bute.

Opening Times: All year: daily.

Admission: Free.

STIRLING CASTLE

CASTLE WYND, STIRLING FK8 1EJ

Owner: Historic Scotland   *Contact:* Jon MacNeil

Tel: 01786 450000 **Fax:** 01786 464678

Stirling Castle has played a key role in Scottish history, dominating the North–South and East–West routes through Scotland. The battles of Stirling Bridge and Bannockburn were fought in its shadow and Mary Queen of Scots lived here as a child. Marvellous Renaissance architecture and interpretive displays.

Location: OS Ref. NS790 941. At the top of Castle Wynd in Stirling.

Opening Times: Apr - Sept: 9.30am - 6pm. Oct - Mar: 9.30am - 5pm, last ticket 45 mins before closing.

Admission: Adult £5, Child £1.50, Conc. £3.75. 10% discount for groups (10+). Free booked school visits, except July & August.

Picnic area. Joint ticket with Argyll's Lodging. Private hire. Partially suitable. WC. Licensed. P Guide dogs only.

Stirling Castle Heads, West Highlands.

TOROSAY CASTLE & GARDENS

CRAIGNURE, ISLE OF MULL PA65 6AY

Owner/Contact: Mr Chris James

Tel: 01680 812421 **Fax:** 01680 812470 **e-mail:** torosay@aol.com

Torosay Castle and Gardens set on the magnificent Island of Mull, was completed in 1858 by the eminent architect David Bryce in the Scottish baronial style, and is surrounded by 12 acres of spectacular gardens which offer an exciting contrast between formal terraces, impressive statue walk and informal woodland, also rhododendron collection, alpine, walled, bog and oriental gardens. The house offers family history, portraits, scrapbooks and antiques in an informal and relaxed atmosphere.

Location: OS Ref. NM730 350. 1¹/₂ m SE of Craignure by A849. 2m W of Duart Castle.

Opening Times: House: Easter - mid-Oct: daily, 10.30am - 5.30pm, last admission 5pm. Gardens: All year: daily, 9am - 7pm or daylight hours in winter.

Admission: Adult £4.50, Child £1.50, Conc. £3.50. Groups: Adult £3.50, Child £1, Conc. £3.50.

 Grounds suitable. WC. In grounds, on leads.

YOUNGER BOTANIC GARDEN BENMORE

Dunoon, Argyll PA23 8QU

Tel: 01369 706261
Fax: 01369 706369

Contact: The Curator

A botanical paradise. Enter the magnificent avenue of giant redwoods and follow trails through the Formal Garden and hillside woodlands to a viewpoint with its spectacular outlook over the Holy Loch and the Eachaig Valley. World-famous collections of rhododendrons and conifers.

Location: OS Ref. NS150 850. 7m N of Dunoon on A815.

Opening Times: 1 Mar - 31 Oct: daily, 9.30am - 6pm.

Admission: Adult £3, Child £1, Conc. £2.50, Family £7. Group discounts available.

 Licensed. By arrangement. P
In grounds, on leads.

Stirling Castle Heads, West Highlands.

Kilchurn Castle.

Grampian

Bennachie. Aberdeen & Grampian Tourist Board.

CONTACT

The Chamberlain
Duff House
Banff
AB45 3SX

Tel: 01261 818181

Fax: 01261 818900

LOCATION

OS Ref. NT691 634

Banff. 47m NE of
Aberdeen on A947.

DUFF HOUSE
Banff

DUFF HOUSE is one of the most imposing and palatial houses in Scotland, with a strong classical façade and a grand staircase leading to the main entrance. It remained in the hands of the Duffs, Dukes of Fife, until 1906 when the family presented the estate to Banff and Macduff, consigning its contents to the saleroom.

Since then it has had a colourful history as an hotel, sanatorium and prisoner-of-war camp, before being taken into the care of Historic Scotland in 1956. After a comprehensive programme of structural repairs and extensive conservation and restoration, Duff House opened to the public as an outstation of the National Galleries of Scotland in April 1995.

Set in acres of parkland, by the banks of the River Deveron, Duff House is one of the glories of the North East. Designed by William Adam for William Duff (1st Earl Fife), it is dramatically sited next to the Royal Burgh of Banff and the fishing port of Macduff and is a splendid example of Scottish baroque architecture.

Drawn from the rich holdings of the National Galleries, highlights of the picture display include El Greco's *St Jerome in Penitence*, J G Cuyp's *Dutch Family Group*, and Allan Ramsay's magnificent full length portrait of Elizabeth Cunyngham has been transformed by recent cleaning, revealing a wonderfully subtle range of colours.

OPENING TIMES

SUMMER

1 April - 30 September
Daily: 11am - 5pm.

WINTER

1 October - 31 March
Thur - Sun
11am - 4pm.

ADMISSION

Adult	£3.00
Conc	£2.00
Family	£7.00
Groups (10+)	£2.00

Free admission to shop, tearoom, grounds and woodland walks.

Free wedding photography permitted in grounds. Wedding photography permitted in vestibule for fee of £50.

CONFERENCE/FUNCTION	
ROOM	MAX CAPACITY
Long Gallery	100
Vestibule	65
Dining Room Salon	80
North Drawing Room	40

Audio-visual room, baby changing facilities, playground, assault course, woodland walks. Croquet and French boules equipment available for hire.

Special functions, corporate hospitality, conferences.

Access & parking, lift to gallery floor, wheelchairs. WC.

Tearoom serving light lunches. Open: 11am - 4pm.

Car and coach parking free, 4 coach spaces, coaches to book.

Schools admitted free, teachers' pack, education suite, teachers encouraged to pre-visit free.

ARBUTHNOTT HOUSE

Tel: 01561 361226 **Fax:** 01561 320476

Arbuthnott, Laurencekirk AB30 1PA

e-mail: keith@arbuth.u-net.com

Owner: The Viscount of Arbuthnott   **Contact:** The Master of Arbuthnott

Arbuthnott family home for 800 years with formal 17th century walled garden on unusually steep south facing slope. Well maintained grass terraces, herbaceous borders, shrubs and greenhouses.

Location: OS Ref. NO796 751. Off B967 between A90 and A92, 25m S of Aberdeen.

Opening Times: House: 2/3 & 30/31 May, 11/12 Jul, 1/2 Aug & 29/30 Aug. Guided tours: 2 - 5pm. Garden: All year, 9am - 5pm.

Admission: House: £3 Garden: £2.

  Ground floor suitable.   Obligatory.   P

BALFLUIG CASTLE

Tel: 0171 624 3200

Alford, Aberdeenshire AB33 8EJ

Owner/Contact: Mark Tennant of Balfluig

Small 16th century tower house in farmland, restored in 1967.

Location: OS Ref. NJ586 151. Alford, Aberdeenshire.

Opening Times: By written appointment to M I Tennant Esq, 30 Abbey Gardens, London NW8 9AT. Occasionally let by the week for holidays. Scottish Tourist Board***.

  Not suitable.   1 single, 4 double.

BALMORAL CASTLE (GROUNDS & EXHIBITIONS)

Tel: 013397 42334/42335

Balmoral, Ballater, Aberdeenshire AB35 5TB   **Fax:** 013397 42271

Owner: Her Majesty The Queen   **Contact:** Captain J R Wilson

Holiday home of the Royal Family, bought by Prince Albert in 1852. Grounds, gardens and exhibition of paintings and works of art in the ballroom.

Location: OS Ref. NO256 951. Off A93 between Ballater and Braemar. 50m W of Aberdeen.

Opening Times: 12 Apr - 31 Jul: daily, 10am - 5pm. Closed Suns in Apr.

Admission: Adult £4, Child (5-16yrs) £1, OAP £3.

        In grounds, on leads.

BALVENIE CASTLE

Tel: 01340 820121

Dufftown

Owner: Historic Scotland   **Contact:** The Custodian

Picturesque ruins of 13th century moated stronghold originally owned by the Comyns. Visited by Edward I in 1304 and by Mary Queen of Scots in 1562. Occupied by Cumberland in 1746.

Location: OS Ref. NJ326 408. At Dufftown on A941.

Opening Times: 1 Apr - 30 Sept: daily, 9.30am - 6.30pm, last ticket 6pm.

Admission: Adult £1.20, Child 50p, Conc. 90p.

Huntly Castle. Grampian Highlands.

Historic Scotland

BRAEMAR CASTLE

BRAEMAR, ABERDEENSHIRE AB35 5XR

Owner: *Capt A A C Farquharson of Invercauld*   **Contact:** *Bruce & Carrol McCudden*

Tel/Fax: 013397 41219 **e-mail:** invercauld@aol.com

Braemar Castle has been the ancestral home of the Clan Farquharson for over 200 years. The 'Black' Colonel of Inverey, the enemy clan leader, attacked and burned the castle in 1689 and after being rebuilt was garrisoned by Hanoverian troops for some 60 years after the 1745 Jacobite rebellion. In some of the rooms you can see the 'graffiti' of the English soldiers. Nowadays, the castle is peaceful, and this family home attracts thousands of visitors each year to see the impressive selection of furnished rooms covering decades of the Farquharson history. A massive iron yett leads you to the pit dungeon, which was a gruesome place in years gone by.

Location: OS Ref. NO156 924. 1/2 m NE of Braemar on A93.

Opening Times: Easter Fri - end Oct: Sat - Thur (plus Fris in Jul & Aug), 10am - 6pm.

Admission: Adult £2.50, Child £1, Conc. £2.

  Picnic area.   Not suitable.   By arrangement.   P
In grounds on leads.

BRODIE CASTLE

FORRES, MORAY IV36 0TE

Owner: *The National Trust for Scotland*   **Contact:** *Dr Stephanie Blackden*

Tel: 01309 641371 **Fax:** 01309 641600

This imposing Castle stands in rich Morayshire parkland. The lime harled building is a typical 'Z' plan tower house with ornate corbelled battlements and bartizans, with 17th & 19th century additions. The interior has unusual plaster ceilings, a major art collection, porcelain and fine furniture. There is a woodland walk by a large pond with access to wildlife observation hides. In springtime the grounds are carpeted with many varieties of daffodils for which Brodie Castle is rightly famous.

Location: OS Ref. NH980 577. Off A96 4 1/2 m W of Forres and 24m E of Inverness.

Opening Times: Castle: 1 Apr - 3 Oct: Mon - Sat, 11am - 5.30pm. Suns, 1.30 - 5.30pm, weekends in Oct: Sats, 11am - 5.30pm, Suns, 1.30 - 5.30pm. Last admission 4.30pm. Other times by appointment. Grounds: all year, daily, 9.30am - sunset.

Admission: Adult £4.40, Conc. £2.90, Family £11.70. Groups: Adult £3.50, Schools £1.

    In grounds, on leads.

Grampian
Scotland

CASTLE FRASER & GARDEN

SAUCHEN, INVERURIE AB51 7LD

Owner: The National Trust for Scotland   *Contact: Eric Wilkinson*

Tel: 01330 833463

Over 400 years of history could be told if the stout walls of Castle Fraser could speak. Begun in 1575 by the 6th Laird, Michael Fraser, the two low wings contribute to the scale and magnificence of the towers rising above them, combining to make this the largest and most elaborate of the Scottish castles built on the 'Z' plan. The stunning simplicity of the Great Hall, which occupies the entire first floor of the main block, with its striking fireplace, almost 3 metres wide, immediately creates for the visitor the atmosphere of past centuries.

Location: OS Ref. NJ723 125. Off A944, 4m N of Dunecht & 16m W of Aberdeen.

Opening Times: Castle: Good Fri - Easter Mon, 1 May - 30 Jun & 1 Sept - 3 Oct: daily, 1.30 - 5.30pm. 1 Jul - 31 Aug: daily, 11am - 5.30pm, weekends in Oct, 1.30 - 5.30pm, last adm. 4.45pm. Tearoom: as castle, opens 11am. Garden: all year, daily, 9.30am - 6pm. Grounds: all year, daily, 9.30am - sunset.

Admission: Adult £4.40, Child/Conc. £2.90. Groups: Adult £3.50. School £1. Family £11.70. Garden & grounds only: Adult £2, Child £1.30, Groups: Adult £1.60, Child/School £1.

CANDACRAIG GARDEN & GALLERY   Tel: 01975 651226 Fax: 01975 651391

Candacraig Gardens, Strathdon AB36 8XT

Owner/Contact: Harry Young

1820s B listed walled display garden, art gallery and specialist plant nursery. Wedding ceremonies conducted in beautiful Victorian Gothic marriage room. Marquees in garden for receptions, garden parties, picnics, barbecues and small business conferences. Telephone, fax and video facilities. Floodlights in evening.

Location: OS Ref. NJ339 110. On A944 1½ m SW of Strathdon, 20m from Alford.

Opening Times: 1 May - 30 Sept: daily, 10am - 6pm.

Admission: Donation box. Pre-arranged groups: Adult £1, Child Free.

   By arrangement. Limited for coaches. Guide dogs only.
1 single, 1 double (self-catering).

CORGARFF CASTLE   Tel: 013398 83635

Strathdon

Owner: Historic Scotland   **Contact:** The Custodian

A 16th century tower house converted into a barracks for Hanoverian troops in 1748. Its last military use was to control the smuggling of illicit whisky between 1827 and 1831. Still complete and with star-shaped fortification.

Location: OS Ref. NJ255 086. 8m W of Strathdon on A939. 14m NW of Ballater.

Opening Times: 1 Apr - 30 Sept: daily, 9.30am - 6.30pm. 1 Oct - 31 Mar: Sats, 9.30am - 4.30pm. Suns, 2 - 4.30pm, last admission ½ hr before closing.

Admission: Adult £2.50, Child £1, Conc. £1.90.

CRAIGSTON CASTLE   Tel: 01888 551228/551640

Turriff, Aberdeenshire AB53 5PX

Owner: William Pratesi Urquhart   **Contact:** Mrs Fiona Morrison

Built in 1607 to John Urquhart Tutor of Cromarty's individualistic plan. An arch and ornate sculptured balcony joins two towers, one noticeably wider than the other, to accommodate the Laird's private apartments. The largely unchanged interior, still lived in by the Urquhart family, includes carved portraits of the Scottish Kings and much else.

Location: OS Ref. NJ762 550. On B9105, 4½ m NE of Turrif.

Opening Times: 31 Jul - 15 Aug: daily (closed Mon & Tue), 10am - 4pm. 21 - 30 Aug: daily (closed Mon & Tue), 10am - 4pm. Also groups throughout the year by appointment.

Admission: Adult £3, Child £1, OAP £2, Student £1.50.

  Not suitable. Obligatory. P In grounds on leads.

CRATHES CASTLE

Harvey Wood

BANCHORY AB31 3QJ

Owner: The National Trust for Scotland   *Contact: The Property Administrator*

Tel: 01330 844525   **Fax:** 01330 844797

Fairytale-like turrets, gargoyles of fantastic design, superb painted ceilings and the ancient Horn of Leys given in 1323 to Alexander Burnett by King Robert the Bruce, are just a few of the exciting features at this most picturesque castle. The building of the castle began in 1553 and took 40 years to complete. Just over 300 years later, Sir James and Lady Burnett began developing the walled garden and created not just one but eight superb gardens which now provide a riot of colour throughout the summer.

Location: OS Ref. NO733 969. On A93, 3m E of Banchory and 15m W of Aberdeen.

Opening Times: Castle, visitor centre, shop & restaurant: 1 Apr - 31 Oct: daily, 11am - 5.30pm, last admission to castle 4.45pm. Plant sales: same dates except weekends only in Oct. Other times by appointment only. Garden & grounds: all year, daily, 9.30am - sunset. Timed tickets - limited number available each day.

Admission: Adult £5, Conc. £3.40, Family £13.50. Group: Adult £4, School £1. Grounds only: Adult £2, Conc. £1.30.

CRUICKSHANK BOTANIC GARDEN   Tel: 01224 272704 Fax: 01224 272703

St Machar Drive, Aberdeen AB24 3UU

Owner: University of Aberdeen   **Contact:** R B Rutherford

Extensive collection of shrubs, herbaceous and alpine plants and trees. Rock and water gardens.

Location: OS Ref. NJ938 084. In old Aberdeen.

Opening Times: All year: Mon - Fri, 9am - 4.30pm. May - Sept: Sat & Sun, 2 - 5pm.

Admission: Free.

  Grounds suitable. P No parking. In grounds, on leads.

DALLAS DHU DISTILLERY   Tel: 01309 676548

Forres

Owner: Historic Scotland   **Contact:** The Custodian

A completely preserved time capsule of the distiller's craft. Wander at will through this fine old Victorian distillery then enjoy a dram. Visitor centre, shop and audio-visual theatre.

Location: OS Ref. NJ035 566. 1m S of Forres off the A940.

Opening Times: 1 Apr - 30 Sept: daily, 9.30am - 6.30pm, last ticket 6pm. 1 Oct - 31 Mar: Mon - Sat, 9.30am - 4.30pm, Suns, 2 - 4.30pm, last ticket 4pm. Closed Thur pm and Fris in winter.

Admission: Adult £2.50, Child £1, Conc. £1.90.

DELGATIE CASTLE

TURRIFF, ABERDEENSHIRE AB53 5TD

Owner: Delgatie Castle Trust   **Contact:** Mrs Joan Johnson

Tel: 01888 563479 **Fax:** 01888 563479

11th century castle which has largely remained in the Hay family for the last 650 years and is now officially the Clan Hay centre. Mary Queen of Scots stayed here in 1562. Her bed-chamber is on view. Painted ceilings dated 1592 and 1597. Widest turnpike stair of its kind in Scotland. Lake and woodland walks.

Location: OS Ref. NJ754 506. Off A947 Aberdeen to Banff Road.

Opening Times: 2 Apr - 25 Oct: 10am - 5pm.

Admission: Adult £2.50, Child/OAP £1.50.

Ground floor suitable. WC. Home-baking. By arrangement. Guide dogs only.

DRUM CASTLE

Tel: 01330 811204

Drumoak, by Banchory AB31 3EY

Owner: The National Trust for Scotland   **Contact:** The Property Manager

The combination over the years of a 13th century square tower, a very fine Jacobean mansion house and the additions of the Victorian lairds make Drum Castle unique among Scottish castles. Owned for 653 years by one family, the Irvines, every stone and every room is steeped in history. Superb furniture and paintings provide a visual feast for visitors. In the 16th century chapel, the stained glass windows, the font copied from the Saxon one in Winchester Cathedral and the Augsburg silver Madonna, all add immense interest for visitors.

Location: OS Ref. NJ796 004. Off A93, 3m W of Peterculter and 10m W of Aberdeen.

Opening Times: Castle: Good Fri - Easter Mon, 1 May - 30 Sept: daily, 1.30 - 5.30pm. Weekends in Oct: 1.30 - 5.30pm, last admission 4.45pm. Garden; same dates, daily 10am - 6pm. Grounds; all year, daily, 9.30 - sunset.

Admission: Adult £4.40, Child £2.90, Family £11.70. Groups: Adult £3.50, School £1. Group visits must book. Gardens & grounds only: Adult £2, Child £1.30. Groups: Adult £1.60, School £1.

DRUMMUIR CASTLE

Tel: 01542 810332 **Fax:** 01542 810302

Drummuir, by Keith, Banffshire AB55 5JE

Owner: The Gordon-Duff Family   **Contact:** Liz Robson

Castellated Victorian Gothic-style castle built in 1847 by Admiral Duff. 60ft high lantern tower with fine plasterwork. Family portraits, interesting artefacts and other paintings. Organic walled garden and plant sales.

Location: OS Ref. NO881 839. Midway between Keith (5m) and Dufftown, off the B9014.

Opening Times: 28/29 Aug, 4/5 & 8 - 29 Sept: inclusive tours at 2pm & 3pm.

Admission: Adult £2, Child £1.50. Pre-arranged groups: Adult £2, Child £1.50.

Obligatory. In grounds on leads.

DUFF HOUSE

See page 68 for full page entry.

DUNNOTTAR CASTLE

Tel: 01569 762173

The Lodge, Stonehaven AB39 2TL   **Contact:** P McKenzie

Spectacular ruin. Impregnable fortress to the Earls Marischals of Scotland. The site for the successful protection of the Scottish Crown Jewels against the might of Cromwell's army. A castle dreams are made of. A must for anyone who takes Scottish history seriously.

Location: OS Ref. NO881 839. Just off A92. 1½ m SE of Stonehaven.

Opening Times: Easter - Oct: Mon - Sat, 9am - 6pm. Suns, 2 - 5pm. Nov - Easter: Mon - Fri, 9am - sunset. Closed weekends when clocks change. Last admission: 30 mins before closing.

Admission: Adult £3, Child £1.

Not suitable. P In grounds, on leads.

DUTHIE PARK & WINTER GARDENS

Tel: 01224 585310 **Fax:** 01224 210532

Polmuir Road, Aberdeen, Grampian Highlands AB11 7TH

Owner: Duthie Park Trust   **Contact:** G Perk Esq

45 acres of parkland and gardens.

Location: OS Ref. NJ97 044. Just N of River Dee, 1m S of city centre.

Opening Times: All year: daily from 9.30pm.

Admission: Free.

Licensed. By arrangement. P Limited for coaches. Guide dogs only.

ELGIN CATHEDRAL

Tel: 01343 547171

Elgin

Owner: Historic Scotland   **Contact:** The Custodian

When entire this was perhaps the most beautiful of Scottish cathedrals, known as the Lantern of the North. 13th century, much modified after almost being destroyed in 1390 by Alexander Stewart, the infamous 'Wolf of Badenoch'. The octagonal chapterhouse is the finest in Scotland. You can see the Bishop's home at Spynie Palace, 2m north of the town.

Location: OS Ref. NJ223 630. In Elgin on the A96.

Opening Times: 1 Apr - 30 Sept: daily, 9.30am - 6.30pm, last ticket 6pm. 1 Oct - 31 Mar: Mon - Sat, 9.30am - 4.30pm, Suns, 2 - 4.30pm, last ticket 4pm. Closed Thur pm & Fris in winter.

Admission: Adult £2, Child £1, Conc. £1.50. Joint entry ticket with Spynie Palace: Adult £2.80, Child £1.20, Conc. £2.10.

FASQUE

Tel: 01561 340202 / 340569 **Fax:** 01561 340325

Fettercairn, Kincardineshire AB30 1DJ

Owner: Charles Gladstone   **Contact:** The Administrator

Example of a Victorian 'upstairs - downstairs' stately home. Inside very little has changed since Victorian times.

Location: OS Ref. NO648 755. On the B974, 1m N of Fettercairn, 4m from A90. Aberdeen/ Dundee 35m.

Opening Times: 1 May - 30 Sept: daily, 11am - 5.30pm. Groups by arrangement any time.

Admission: Adult £3.50, Child £1.50, Conc. £2.50.

Ground floor suitable. By arrangement. P In grounds, on leads.

Drum Castle, Grampian Highlands.

FYVIE CASTLE

TURRIFF, ABERDEENSHIRE AB53 8JS

Owner: *The National Trust for Scotland*   **Contact:** *Clare White*

Tel: 01651 891266   **Fax:** 01651 891107

The south front of this magnificent building employs a plethora of crow-stepped gables, turrets, sculpted dormers and finials in the form of musicians, to create a marvellous façade. The five towers of the castle bear witness to the five families who have owned it. Fyvie Castle boasts the finest wheel stair in Scotland and there is a superb collection of arms and armour and paintings, including works by Batoni, Raeburn, Romney, Gainsborough, Opie and Hoppner.

Location: OS Ref. NJ763 393. Off A947, 8m SE of Turriff, and 25m N of Aberdeen.

Opening Times: Good Fri - Easter Mon, 1 May - 30 Jun & 1 Sept - 3 Oct: daily, 1.30 - 5.30pm. 1 Jul - 31 Aug: daily, 11am - 5.30pm. Weekends in Oct: 1.30 - 5.30pm (last admission 4.45pm). Tearoom: as castle but 12.30pm when castle opens at 1.30pm. Grounds: all year, daily, 9.30am - sunset.

Admission: Adult £4.40, Conc. £2.90, Family £11.70. Groups: Adult £3.50, School £1.

HADDO HOUSE

TARVES, ELLON, ABERDEENSHIRE AB41 0ER

Owner: *The National Trust for Scotland*   **Contact:** *Craig Ferguson*

Tel: 01651 851440   **Fax:** 01651 851888

This appealing house was designed by William Adam in 1731 for William, 2nd Earl of Aberdeen. Much of the splendid interior is 'Adam Revival' carried out about 1880 for John, 7th Earl and 1st Marquess of Aberdeen and his Countess, Ishbel. It is arguably the most elegant house in the north east, a classic English-style stately home transplanted to Scotland. Features of the house include the Italianate sweeping twin staircases at the front of the house, the atmospheric library and the subtlety of the great curving corridor.

Location: OS Ref. NJ868 348. Off B999, 4m N of Pitmedden, 10m NW of Ellon.

Opening Times: House: Good Fri - Easter Mon, 1 May - 3 Oct: daily, 1.30 - 5.30pm. Weekends in Oct: 1.30 - 5.30pm, last admission 4.45pm. Shop & restaurant: Good Fri - 3 Oct: daily, 11am - 5.30pm. Weekends in Oct: 11am - 5.30pm. Garden & country park; all year, daily, 9.30am - sunset.

Admission: Adult £4.40, Conc. £2.90, Family £11.70. Groups: Adult £3.50, School £1.

HUNTLY CASTLE   **Tel:** 01466 793191

Huntly

Owner: Historic Scotland   **Contact:** The Custodian

Known also as Strathbogie Castle, this glorious ruin stands in a beautiful setting on the banks of the River Deveron. Famed for its fine heraldic sculpture and inscribed stone friezes.

Location: OS Ref. NJ532 407. In Huntly on the A96. N side of the town.

Opening Times: 1 Apr - 30 Sept: daily, 9.30am - 6.30pm, last ticket 6pm. 1 Oct - 31 Mar: Mon - Sat, 9.30am - 4.30pm, Suns, 2 - 4.30pm, last ticket 4pm. Closed Thur pm & Fris in winter.

Admission: Adult £2.50, Child £1, Conc £1.90.

KILDRUMMY CASTLE   **Tel:** 01975 571331

Alford, Aberdeenshire

Owner: Historic Scotland   **Contact:** The Custodian

Though ruined, the best example in Scotland of a 13th century castle with a curtain wall, four round towers, hall and chapel of that date. The seat of the Earls of Mar, it was dismantled after the first Jacobite rising in 1715.

Location: OS Ref. NJ455 164. 10m W of Alford on the A97. 16m SSW of Huntley.

Opening Times: 1 Apr - 30 Sept: daily, 9.30am - 6.30pm, last ticket 6pm.

Admission: Adult £1.80, Child 75p, Conc. £1.30.

KILDRUMMY CASTLE GARDEN   **Tel:** 01975 571203 / 571277

Kildrummy, Aberdeenshire   **Contact:** Alastair J Laing

Ancient quarry, shrub and alpine gardens renowned for their interest and variety. Water gardens below ruined castle.

Location: OS Ref. NJ455 164. On A97 off A944 10m SW of Alford. 16m SSW of Huntley.

Opening Times: Apr - Oct: daily, 10am - 5pm.

Admission: Adult £2, Child free.

Partially suitable. By arrangement. In grounds, on leads.

LEITH HALL   **Tel:** 01464 831216   **Fax:** 01464 831594

Huntly, Aberdeenshire AB54 4NQ

Owner: The National Trust for Scotland   **Contact:** The Property Manager

This mansion house is built around a courtyard and was the home of the Leith family for almost 400 years. With an enviable family record of military service over the centuries, the house contains a unique collection of military memorabilia displayed in an exhibition *'For Crown and Country'*. The graciously furnished rooms are a delight to wander through and present a fine impression of the lifestyle of the Leith family.

Location: OS Ref. NJ541 298. B9002, 1m W of Kennethmont, 7m S of Huntley.

Opening Times: House & tearoom: Good Fri - Easter Mon, 1 May - 3 Oct: daily, 1.30 - 5.30pm. Weekends in Oct: 1.30 - 5.30pm, last admission 4.45pm. Gardens & grounds; all year, daily, 9.30am - sunset.

Admission: Adult £4.40, Conc. £2.90, Family £11.70. Groups: Adult £3.50, School £1. Gardens & grounds: Adult £2, Conc. £1.30. Groups: Adult £1.60, School £1.

Partially suitable. WC.

MONYMUSK WALLED GARDEN   **Tel:** 01467 651543

Home Farm, Monymusk, Aberdeen AB51 7HL

Owner/Contact: Mrs E Whyte

Mainly herbaceous plants in walled garden setting.

Opening Times: Nov - Mar: Mon, Wed, Fri & Sat, 10am - 3pm, Suns, 12 noon - 3pm. Apr - Oct: Mon - Sat, 10am - 5pm, Suns, 12 noon - 5pm.

Admission: Donations welcome.

Leith Hall, Grampian Highlands.

PITMEDDEN GARDEN

Doug Westland

ELLON, ABERDEENSHIRE AB41 0PD

Owner: The National Trust for Scotland   *Contact:* The Property Manager

Tel: 01651 842352   **Fax:** 01651 843188

The centrepiece of this property is the Great Garden which was originally laid out in 1675 by Sir Alexander Seton, 1st Baronet of Pitmedden. The elaborate designs, inspired by the garden at the Palace of Holyroodhouse in Edinburgh, have been painstakingly recreated for the enjoyment of visitors. The 100 acre estate contains the very fine Museum of Farming Life, which presents a vivid picture of the lives and times of bygone days when the horse was the power in front of the plough and farm machinery was less complicated than it is today.

Location: OS Ref. NJ885 280. On A920 1m W of Pitmedden village and 14m N of Aberdeen.

Opening Times: Garden, visitor centre, museum, grounds and other facilities: 1 May - 30 Sept: daily, 10am - 5.30pm, last admission 5pm.

Admission: Adult £3.90, Child £2.60, Family £10.40. Groups: Adult £3.20, School £1.

PROVOST SKENE'S HOUSE

45 GUEST ROW, OFF BROAD STREET, ABERDEEN AB10 1AS

Owner: Aberdeen City Council   *Contact:* Christine Rew

Tel: 01224 641086   **Fax:** 01224 632133

Built in the 16th century, Provost Skene's House is one of Aberdeen's few remaining examples of early Burgh architecture. Splendid room settings include a suite of Georgian rooms, an Edwardian nursery, magnificent 17th century plaster ceilings and wood panelling. The painted gallery houses the most important cycle of religious painting in North East Scotland.

Location: OS Ref. NJ943 064. Aberdeen city centre, off Broad Street.

Opening Times: All year: Mon - Sat, 10am - 5pm (closed 25/26/31 Dec & 1/2 Jan).

Admission: Adult £2.50, Conc. £1.50, Family £6, Child (under 5yrs) Free. Groups (10+): 10% discount.

No photography in house.   Small functions.   Not suitable.   By arrangement.   Nearby.   Guide dogs only.

PLUSCARDEN ABBEY

Tel: 01343 890257   **Fax:** 01343 890258

Nr Elgin, Moray IV30 8UA   **Contact:** Father Giles

Valliscaulian, founded 1230.

Location: OS Ref. NJ142 576. On a minor road 6m SW of Elgin. Follow B9010 for first mile.

Opening Times: All year: 4.45am - 8.30pm. Shop open 8.30am - 5pm.

Admission: Free.

Retreats.   Partially suitable. WCs. Won access award.   By arrangement.   In grounds, on leads.   24 singles.

Aberdeen & Grampian Tourist Board

Crovie, Grampian Highlands.

ST MACHAR'S CATHEDRAL TRANSEPTS

Tel: 0131 668 8800

Old Aberdeen

Owner: Historic Scotland

The nave and towers of the Cathedral remain in use as a church, and the ruined transepts are in care. In the south transept is the fine altar tomb of Bishop Dunbar (1514 - 32).

Location: OS Ref. NJ939 088. In old Aberdeen. 1/2 m N of King's College.

Admission: Free.

SPYNIE PALACE

Tel: 01343 546358

Elgin

Owner: Historic Scotland   **Contact:** The Custodian

Spynie Palace was the residence of the Bishops of Moray from the 14th century to 1686. The site is dominated by the massive tower built by Bishop David Stewart (1461-77) and affords spectacular views across Spynie Loch.

Location: OS Ref. NJ231 659. 2m N of Elgin off the A941.

Opening Times: 1 Apr - 30 Sept: daily, 9.30am - 6.30pm. 1 Oct - 31 Mar: Sats, 9.30am - 4.30pm, Suns, 2 - 4.30pm. Last ticket 30 mins before closing.

Admission: Adult £1.80, Child 75p, Conc. £1.30. Joint entry ticket with Elgin Cathedral: Adult £2.80, Child £1.20, Conc. £2.10.

TOLQUHON CASTLE

Tel: 01651 851286

Aberdeenshire

Owner: Historic Scotland   **Contact:** The Custodian

Tolquhon was built for the Forbes family. The early 15th century tower was enlarged between 1584 and 1589 with a large mansion around the courtyard. Noted for its highly ornamented gatehouse and pleasance.

Location: OS Ref. NJ874 286. 15m N of Aberdeen on the A920. 6m N of Ellon.

Opening Times: 1 Apr - 30 Sept: daily, 9.30am - 6.30pm. 1 Oct - 31 Mar: Sats, 9.30am - 4.30pm, Suns, 2 - 4.30pm. Last ticket 30 mins before closing.

Admission: Adult £1.80, Child 75p, Conc. £1.30.

Highlands & Skye

Liathach from Loch Clair, Torridon. Highlands of Scotland Tourist Board.

CAWDOR CASTLE
Nairn

Owner: The Dowager Countess Cawdor

CONTACT

The Secretary
Cawdor Castle
Nairn
Scotland
IV12 5RD

Tel: 01667 404615

Fax: 01667 404674

e-mail: cawdor.castle@
btinternet.com

LOCATION

OS Ref. NH850 500

From Edinburgh
A9, 3½ hrs,
Inverness 20 mins,
Nairn 10 mins.
Main road: A9, 14m.

Rail: Nairn Station
5m.

Bus: Inverness to Nairn
bus route 200 yds.

Taxi: Nairn Taxis
01667 455342.

Air: Inverness Airport 5m.

This splendid romantic castle dating from the late 14th century was built as a private fortress by the Thanes of Cawdor, and remains the home of the Cawdor family to this day. The ancient medieval tower was built around the legendary holly tree.

Although the house has evolved over 600 years, later additions mainly of the 17th century were all built in the Scottish vernacular style with slated roofs over walls and crow-stepped gables of mellow local stone. This style gives Cawdor a strong sense of unity, and the massive, severe exterior belies an intimate interior that gives the place a surprisingly personal, friendly atmosphere.

Good furniture, fine portraits and pictures,

interesting objects and outstanding tapestries are arranged to please the family rather than to echo fashion or impress. Memories of Shakespeare's *Macbeth* give Cawdor an elusive, evocative quality that delights visitors.

GARDENS

The flower garden also has a family feel to it, where plants are chosen out of affection rather than affectation. This is a lovely spot between spring and late summer. The walled garden has been restored with a holly maze, paradise garden, knot garden and thistle garden. The wild garden beside its stream leads into beautiful trails through a spectacular mature mixed woodland, through which paths are helpfully marked and colour-coded.

OPENING TIMES

SUMMER

1 May - 10 October
Daily: 10am - 5.30pm.

Last admission 5pm.

WINTER

11 October - 30 April
Closed.

ADMISSION

SUMMER
House & Garden

Adult	£5.40
Child (5-15yrs)	£2.80
OAP/Student	£4.40
Family (2+5)	£14.50

Groups (20+)

Adult	£4.90
Child (5-15yrs)	£2.40
OAP/Student	£4.40

Garden only

Per person	£2.80

CONFERENCE/FUNCTION		
ROOM	SIZE	MAX CAPACITY
Cawdor Hall		40

ℹ️ 9 hole golf course, putting green, golf clubs for hire, Conferences, whisky tasting, musical entertainments, specialised garden visits. No photography, video taping or tripods inside.

🎁 Gift, book and wool shops.

🍽 Lunches, sherry or champagne receptions.

♿ Visitors may alight at the entrance. WC. Only ground floor accessible.

🍴 Licensed buttery, May-Oct, groups should book.

🅿 250 cars and 25 coaches. Two weeks' notice for group catering, coach drivers/couriers free.

🖼 £2.40 per child. Room notes, quiz and answer sheet can be provided. Ranger service and nature trails.

🛡 SPECIAL EVENTS

• **JUN 5/6:**
Special Gardens Weekend: Guided tours of gardens and Cawdor Big Wood.

DUNVEGAN CASTLE
Isle of Skye

Owner: John Macleod of Macleod

CONTACT

The Administrator
Dunvegan Castle
Isle of Skye
Scotland
IV55 8WF

Tel: 01470 521206

Fax: 01470 521205

e-mail: info@
dunvegancastle.com

LOCATION

OS Ref. NG250 480

1m N of village. NW corner of Skye.

From Inverness A82 to Invermoriston, A887 to Kyle of Lochalsh 82m. From Fort William A82 to Invergarry, A87 to Kyle of Lochalsh 76m.

Kyle of Lochalsh to Dunvegan 45m via Skye Bridge (toll).

Ferry: To the Isle of Skye, 'roll-on, roll-off', 30 minute crossing.

Rail: Inverness to Kyle of Lochalsh 3 - 4 trains per day - 45m.

Bus: Portree 25m, Kyle of Lochalsh 45m.

DUNVEGAN is unique. It is the only Great House in the Western Isles of Scotland to have retained its family and its roof. It is the oldest home in the whole of Scotland continuously inhabited by the same family – the Chiefs of the Clan Macleod. A Castle placed on a rock by the sea - the curtain wall is dated before 1200 AD – its superb location recalls the Norse Empire of the Vikings, the ancestors of the Chiefs.

Dunvegan's continuing importance as a custodian of the Clan spirit is epitomised by the famous Fairy Flag, whose origins are shrouded in mystery but whose ability to protect both Chief and Clan is unquestioned. To enter Dunvegan is to arrive at a place whose history combines with legend to make a living reality.

GARDENS

The gardens and grounds extend over some ten acres of woodland walks, peaceful formal lawns and a water garden dominated by two spectacular natural waterfalls. The temperate climate aids in producing a fine show of rhododendrons and azaleas, the chief glory of the garden in spring. One is always aware of the proximity of the sea and many garden walks finish at the Castle Jetty, from where traditional boats make regular trips to view the delightful Seal Colony.

❖

ℹ Gift and craft shop. Boat trips to seal colony. Loch cruises, charter and fishing trips, pedigree Highland cattle. No photography in castle.

♿ Visitors may alight at entrance. WC.

🍴 Licensed restaurant, (cap. 70) special rates for groups, menus upon request. Tel: 01470 521310. Open late peak season for evening meals.

🧍 By appointment in English or Gaelic at no extra charge. If requested owner may meet groups, tour time 45mins.

P 120 cars and 10 coaches. Do not attempt to take passengers to Castle Jetty (long walk). If possible please book. Seal boat trip dependent upon weather.

🏫 Welcome by arrangement. Guide available on request.

🐕 In grounds only, on lead.

 4 self-catering units, 3 of which sleep 6 and 1 of which sleeps 7.

OPENING TIMES

SUMMER

22 March - 31 October
Daily: 10am - 5.30pm.
Last admission 5pm.

WINTER

November - March
Daily: 11am - 4pm.
Last admission: 3.30pm.

Closed Christmas Eve, Christmas Day, New Year's Eve and New Year's Day.

ADMISSION

SUMMER

Castle & Gardens
Adult £5.20
Child* (5 -16yrs) £2.60
OAP/Student...........£4.60
Group £4.60

Garden only
Adult £3.70
Child* (5 -16yrs) £2.00

Seal Boats
Adult £3.80
Child* (5 -16yrs) £2.50

Loch Cruises
Adult £8.00
Child £4.00
Conc. £6.50

Guide Books
Castle £3.00
Gardens £2.00
or both for £4.50

*Child under 5 Free.

WINTER

11am - 4pm.
No boat trips.

ATTADALE GARDENS

Tel: 01520 722217 **Fax:** 01520 722546

By Strathcarron, Ross-shire IV54 8YX

Owner/Contact: Mr & Mrs Ewen Macpherson

The garden and woodland walks were planted by the Schroder family from 1890 onwards with species rhododendrons, azaleas and southern hemisphere plants made possible by the warm gulf stream. Spectacular water gardens with primula, iris and giant gunnera. Hill walks with views of Skye and the sea. Victorian sunken garden by the house. Waterproof shoes recommended.

Location: OS Ref. NG920 400. On A890 between Strathcarron and South Strome. 12m N of A87.

Opening Times: 1 Apr - 31 Oct: Mon - Sat, 10am - 5.30pm.

Admission: Adult £2, Child £1. Coaches/guided tours by prior arrangement.

🦽 🅿 🏠 In grounds, on leads.

BALLINDALLOCH CASTLE

GRANTOWN-ON-SPEY, BANFFSHIRE AB37 9AX

Owner: Mr & Mrs Russell   *Contact:* Mrs Clare Russell

Tel: 01807 500206 **Fax:** 01807 500210

Ballindalloch is a much loved family home and one of the few castles lived in continuously by its original owners, the Macpherson-Grants, since 1546. Filled with family memorabilia and a magnificent collection of 17th century Spanish paintings, it is home to the famous breed of Aberdeen Angus cattle. Beautiful rock and rose garden, river walks.

Location: OS Ref. NJ178 366. 14m NE of Grantown-on-Spey on A95, 22m S of Elgin on A95.

Opening Times: Good Fri - 30 Sept: 10am - 5pm.

Admission: House & Grounds: Adult £5, Child (5-16) £2.50, Conc. £4.50, Family (2+3) £13. Grounds only: Adult £2, Child £1. Groups: (20+) Adult £4.50, Child £2.

📷 🦽 Ground floor & grounds. WC. 🔲 🅿 🎧 Audio-visual.
🏠 In grounds, on leads in dog walking area.

CAWDOR CASTLE 🏛

See page 76 for full page entry.

CLAN DONALD VISITOR CENTRE & ARMADALE CASTLE GARDEN

Armadale, Isle of Skye IV45 8RS   **Tel:** 01471 844305 **Fax:** 01471 844275

Owner: Clan Donald Lands Trust   **Contact:** Flora MacLean - Visitor Services Manager

Part of Armadale Castle houses a visitor centre and the 'Museum of the Isles' telling the story of the Macdonalds and the Lords of the Isles.

Location: OS Ref. NG630 020. 1m N of the Mallaig - Armadale ferry terminal.

Opening Times: Apr - Oct: daily, 9.30am - 5.30pm.

Admission: Adult £3.50, Child/Conc./Groups £2.40.

📷 🍽 🦽 Partially suitable. WCs. 🔲🍴 Licensed. 🎿 By arrangement. 🅿
🏠 In grounds, on leads.

CROMARTY COURTHOUSE

Tel: 01381 600418 **Fax:** 01381 600408

Church Street, Cromarty IV11 8XA   **Contact:** David Alston

18th century town courthouse, visitor centre and museum.

Location: OS Ref. NH790 680. 25m N of Inverness.

Opening Times: Apr - Oct: 10am - 5pm. Nov, Dec & Mar: 12 noon - 4pm.

Admission: Adult £3, Conc. £2.

🖼

CULLODEN 👑

Tel: 01463 790607 **Fax:** 01463 794294

Culloden Moor, Inverness IV1 2ED

Owner: The National Trust for Scotland   **Contact:** Ross Mackenzie

No name in Scottish history evokes more emotion than that of Culloden, the bleak moor which in 1746 saw the hopes of the young Prince Charles Edward Stuart crushed, and the end of the Jacobite Rising, the 'Forty-Five'. The Prince's forces, greatly outnumbered by those of the brutal Duke of Cumberland, nevertheless went into battle with a courage which has passed into legend.

Location: OS Ref. NH745 450. On B9006, 5m E of Inverness.

Opening Times: Site; all year, daily. Visitor centre: 1 Feb - 31 Mar & 1 Nov - 31 Dec (except 24 - 26 Dec): daily, 10am - 4pm. 1 Apr - 31 Oct: daily, 9am - 6pm. Restaurant & audio-visual: same dates but closes 30 mins earlier.

Admission: Adult £3.20, Conc. £2.20, Family £8.60. Groups: Adult £2.60, School £1.

ℹ Visitor centre. 🔲 Closed 1 - 6 Nov. 🦽 🍴 🎧 Audio-visual.
🏠 In dog walking area only.

DOCHFOUR GARDENS

Tel: 01463 861218 **Fax:** 01463 861366

Dochgarroch, Inverness IV3 6JY

Owner: Dochfour Estate   **Contact:** Miss J Taylor

Victorian terraced garden near Inverness with panoramic views over Loch Dochfour. Magnificent specimen trees, naturalised daffodils, rhododendrons, water garden, yew topiary.

Location: OS Ref. NH620 610. 6m SW of Inverness on A82 to Fort William.

Opening Times: Gardens: Apr - Sept, Mon - Fri, 10am - 5pm. House not open.

Admission: Garden walk - £1.50.

DUNROBIN CASTLE 🏛

GOLSPIE, SUTHERLAND KW10 6SF

Owner: The Sutherland Trust   *Contact:* Keith Jones, Curator

Tel: 01408 633177 **Fax:** 01408 634081

Dates from the 13th century with additions in the 17th, 18th and 19th centuries. Wonderful furniture, paintings, library, ceremonial robes and memorabilia. Victorian museum in grounds with a fascinating collection including Pictish stones. Set in fine woodlands overlooking the sea. Magnificent formal gardens, one of few remaining French/Scottish formal parterres. Falconry display.

Location: OS Ref. NC850 010. 50m N of Inverness on A9. 1m NE of Golspie.

Opening Times: 1 Apr - 31 May & 1 - 15 Oct: Mon - Sat, 10.30am - 4.30pm. Suns, 12 noon - 4.30pm. 1 Jun - 30 Sept: Mon - Sat, 10.30am - 5.30pm. Suns, 12 noon - 5.30pm.

Admission: Adult £5.50, Child/Conc. £4. Groups: Adult £5, Child/Conc £4. Family (2+2) £16.

📷 🍴

THE DOUNE OF ROTHIEMURCHUS

Tel: 01479 812345

By Aviemore, PH22 1QH

Owner: J P Grant of Rothiemurchus   **Contact:** Rothiemurchus Visitor Centre

The family home of the Grants of Rothiemurchus was nearly lost as a ruin and has been under an ambitious repair programme since 1975. This exciting project may be visited on selected Mondays throughout the year. Book with the visitor centre for a longer 2 hr 'Highland Lady' tour which explores the haunts of Elizabeth Grant of Rothiemurchus, born 1797, author of *Memoirs of a Highland Lady*, who vividly described the Doune and its surroundings from the memories of her childhood.

Location: OS Ref. NH900 100. 2m S of Aviemore on E bank of Spey river.

Opening Times: House: selected Mons. Grounds: May - Aug: Mon, 10am - 12.30pm & 2 - 4.30pm, also 1st Mon in the month during winter.

Admission: House £5. Grounds only: £1. Booking essential.

ⓘ Visitor centre. 📷 ✗ Obligatory. 🅿 Limited. 🐕 In grounds, on leads.

DUNVEGAN CASTLE

See page 77 for full page entry.

EILEAN DONAN CASTLE

Tel: 01599 555202

Dornie, Kyle, Wester IV40 8DX

Contact: The Administrator

Picturesque castle on an islet, dating back to 1220.

Location: OS Ref. NG880 260. On A87 8m E of Skye Bridge.

Opening Times: Easter - end Oct: 10am - 5.30pm.

Admission: Adult £3.75, Conc./Groups £2.50

📷 ♿ Not suitable. 🅿 🐕 In grounds, on leads.

FORT GEORGE

ARDERSIER BY INVERNESS IV1 2TD

Owner: Historic Scotland   *Contact: Tommy Simpson*

Tel: 01667 462777 **Fax:** 01667 462698

Built following the Battle of Culloden to subdue the Highlands, Fort George never saw a shot fired in anger. One of the most outstanding artillery fortifications in Europe with reconstructed barrack room displays. The Queen's Own Highlanders' Museum.

Location: OS Ref. NH762 567. 11m NE of Inverness off the A96 by Ardersier.

Opening Times: Apr - Sept: daily, 9.30am - 6.30pm. Oct - Mar: Mon - Sat, 9.30am - 4.30pm; Suns, 2 - 4.30pm. Last ticket sold 45 mins before closing.

Admission: Adult £3, Child £1, Conc. £2.30. 10% discount for groups (10+).

ⓘ Picnic tables. 📷 ☎ Private evening hire. ♿ Wheelchairs available. WCs. In summer. 🅿 Free if pre-booked. 🐕 In grounds, on leads.

GLENFINNAN

Tel/Fax: 01397 722250

Inverness-shire PH37 4LT

Owner: The National Trust for Scotland   **Contact:** Mrs Lillias Grant

The monument, situated on the scenic road to the Isles, is set amid superb Highland scenery at the head of Loch Shiel. It was erected in 1815 in tribute to the clansmen who fought and died in the Jacobite cause. Prince Charles Edward Stuart's standard was raised near here in 1745. Despite its inspired beginnings, the campaign came to a grim conclusion on the Culloden battlefield in 1746.

Location: OS Ref. NM906 805. On A830, 18m W of Fort William, Lochaber.

Opening Times: Site: all year, daily. Visitor centre & snack bar: 1 Apr - 18 May and 1 Sept - 31 Oct: daily, 10am - 5pm. 19 May - 31 Aug: daily, 9.30am - 6pm (snack bar 10am - 6pm).

Admission: Adult £1.50, Child £1, Family £4.

ⓘ Visitor centre. 📷 ♿ Grounds suitable. WC. 🅿 🐕 In grounds, on leads. Ⓦ

INVEREWE GARDEN

POOLEWE, ROSS & CROMARTY IV22 2LQ

Owner: The National Trust for Scotland   *Contact: Keith Gordon*

Tel: 01445 781200 **Fax:** 01445 781497

Where in Scotland will you see the tallest Australian gum trees in Britain, sweetly scented Chinese rhododendrons, exotic trees from Chile and Blue Nile lilies from South Africa, all growing on a latitude more northerly than Moscow? The answer is Inverewe. Although you are in a remote corner of Wester Ross, you are also in a sheltered garden, blessed by the North Atlantic Drift. In a spectacular lochside setting among pinewoods, Osgood Mackenzie's Victorian dreams have produced a glorious 50 acre mecca for garden lovers.

Location: OS Ref. NG860 820. On A832, by Poolewe, 6m NE of Gairloch, Highland.

Opening Times: Garden: 15 Mar - 31 Oct: daily, 9.30am - 9pm. 1 Nov - 14 Mar: daily, 9.30 - 5pm. Visitor centre & shop: 15 Mar - 31 Oct: daily, 9.30am - 5.30pm. Restaurant: same dates, daily, 10am - 5pm. Guided walks: 15 Apr - 15 Sept: Mon - Fri at 1.30pm.

Admission: Adult £5, Child £3.40, Family £13.50. Groups: Adult £4, School £1.

ⓘ Visitor centre. 📷 ♿ Grounds suitable. WC. ⓨ Licensed. 🅿 No shade for dogs. 🐕 Guide dogs only. Ⓦ

HUGH MILLER'S COTTAGE

Tel: 01381 600245

Cromarty IV11 8XA

Owner: The National Trust for Scotland   **Contact:** Ms Frieda Gostwick

Furnished thatched cottage of c1698, birthplace of eminent geologist and writer Hugh Miller. Exhibition and video.

Location: OS Ref. NH790 680. Via Kessock Bridge & A832, in Cromarty, 22m NE of Inverness.

Opening Times: 1 May - 30 Sept: Mon - Sat, 11am - 1pm & 2 - 5pm. Suns, 2 - 5pm.

Admission: Adult £2, Child £1.30, Family £5.30. Groups: Adult £1.60, School £1.

♿ Not suitable. 🅿 Public parking at shore. 🐕 Guide dogs only. Ⓦ

URQUHART CASTLE

Tel: 01456 450551

Drumnadrochit, Loch Ness

Owner: Historic Scotland   **Contact:** The Custodian

The remains of one of the largest castles in Scotland dominate a rocky promontory on Loch Ness. It fell into decay after 1689. Most of the existing buildings date from the 16th century. A popular viewpoint for monster spotting. Splendid views up and down the loch.

Location: OS Ref. NH531 286. On Loch Ness, 1½ m S of Drumnadrochit on A82.

Opening Times: 1 Apr - 30 Sept: daily, 9.30am - 6.30pm, last ticket 5.45pm. 1 Oct - 31 Mar: daily, 9.30am - 4.30pm, last ticket 3.45pm.

Admission: Adult £3.80, Child £1.20, Conc. £2.80.

Outer Islands

Ponies at Ninian's, Shetland Islands. Shetland Islands Tourist Board.

Outer Islands Scotland

BALFOUR CASTLE

Tel: 01856 711282 **Fax:** 01856 711283

Shapinsay, Orkney Islands KW17 2DY   **e-mail:** balfourcastle@btinternet.com
Owner/Contact: Mrs Lidderdale
Built in 1848.
Location: OS Ref. HY475 164 on Shapinsay Island, 3$^{1}/_{2}$ m NNE of Kirkwall.
Opening Times: Mid-May – mid-Sept: Wed & Sun, 2.30 - 5.30pm.
Admission: £13 including boat fare, guided tour of castle and gardens and afternoon tea.

BISHOP'S & EARL'S PALACES

Tel: 01856 875461

Kirkwall, Orkney
Owner: Historic Scotland   **Contact:** The Custodian
The Bishop's Palace is a 12th century hall-house with a round tower built by Bishop Reid in 1541-48. The adjacent Earl's Palace built in 1607 has been described as the most mature and accomplished piece of Renaissance architecture left in Scotland.
Location: Bishop's Palace: OS Ref. HY447 108. Earl's Palace: OS Ref. HY448 108. In Kirkwall on A960.
Opening Times: 1 Apr - 30 Sept: daily, 9.30am - 6.30pm, last ticket 6pm.
Admission: Adult £1.80, Child 75p, Conc. £1.30. Joint entry ticket available for all the Orkney monuments: Adult £9, Child £2.50, Conc. £7.

BLACK HOUSE

Tel: 01851 710395

Arnol, Isle of Lewis
Owner: Historic Scotland   **Contact:** The Custodian
A traditional Lewis thatched house, fully furnished, complete with attached barn, byre and stockyard. A peat fire burns in the open hearth.
Location: OS Ref. NB320 500. In Arnol village, 11m NW of Stornoway on A858.
Opening Times: 1 Apr - 30 Sept: Mon - Sat, 9.30am - 6.30pm, last ticket 6pm. 1 Oct - 31 Mar: Mon - Thur & Sat, 9.30am - 4.30pm, last ticket 4pm.
Admission: Adult £2, Child £1, Conc. £1.50.

BROCH OF GURNESS

Tel: 01831 579478

Aikerness, Orkney
Owner: Historic Scotland   **Contact:** The Custodian
Protected by three lines of ditch and rampart, the base of the broch is surrounded by a warren of Iron Age buildings.
Location: OS Ref. HY383 268. At Aikerness, about 14m NW of Kirkwall on A966.
Opening Times: 1 Apr - 30 Sept: daily, 9.30am - 6.30pm, last ticket 6pm.
Admission: Adult £2.50, Child £1, Conc. £1.90. Joint entry ticket available for all Orkney monuments: Adult £9, Child £2.50, Conc. £7.

CALANAIS STANDING STONES

Tel: 01851 621422

Calanais, Stornoway, Lewis, Outer Islands
Owner: Historic Scotland
A cross-shaped setting of standing stones, unique in Scotland.
Location: OS Ref. NB213 330. 12m W of Stornaway off A859.
Opening Times: All year: daily, summer 10am - 7pm, winter 10am - 4pm. Visitor centre closed Suns.
Admission: Adult £1.50, Child 50p, Conc. £1.

Calanais Standing Stones, Lewis.

CARRICK HOUSE

Tel: 01857 622260

Carrick, Eday, Orkney KW17 2AB
Owner: Mr & Mrs Joy   **Contact:** Mrs Rosemary Joy
17th century house of 2 storeys, arched entrance to house dated 1633.
Location: OS Ref. NT227 773. N of island of Eday on minor roads W of B9063 just W of the shore of Calf Sound. Regular ferry service.
Opening Times: Please telephone for details.
Admission: Adult £1.50, Child 75p, Conc. £1. (1998 prices)

Shetland Croft.

JARLSHOF PREHISTORIC & NORSE SETTLEMENT

Tel: 01950 460112

Shetland
Owner: Historic Scotland   **Contact:** The Custodian
Over 3 acres of remains spanning 3,000 years from the Stone Age. Oval-shaped Bronze Age houses, Iron Age broch and wheel houses. Viking long houses, medieval farmstead and 16th century laird's house.
Location: OS Ref. HY401 096. At Sumburgh Head, 22m S of Lerwick on the A970.
Opening Times: 1 Apr - 30 Sept: Mon, Wed, Thur, 9.30am - 6.30pm. Last adm. $^{1}/_{2}$ hr before closing.
Admission: Adult £2.50, Child £1, Conc. £1.90.

KIESSIMUL CASTLE

Tel: 01871 810449

Castlebray, Isle of Barra, Western Isles PA80
Owner/Contact: Ian Allen MacNeil of Barra
Home of the Chief of the MacNeil clan. Dating from the 13th century, the castle has been restored to its 17th century condition.
Location: OS Ref. NL670 990. Just S of Castlebay on Barra, by boat S of A888 in Castlebay.
Opening Times: Apr - Sept: Mon Wed & Sat, 2 - 5pm wind and tide permitting. Please telephone to check.
Admission: Boat and entrance to castle: Adult £3, Child 50p

MAES HOWE

Tel: 01856 761606

Orkney
Owner: Historic Scotland   **Contact:** The Custodian
This world-famous tomb was built in Neolithic times, before 2700 BC. The large mound covers a stone-built passage and a burial chamber with cells in the walls. Runic inscriptions tell of how it was plundered of its treasures by Vikings.
Location: OS Ref. NY318 128. 9m W of Kirkwall on the A965.
Opening Times: 1 Apr - 30 Sept: daily, 9.30am - 6.30pm. 1 Oct - 31 Mar: daily, 9.30am - 5pm.
Admission: Adult £2.50, Child £1, Conc. £1.90. Joint entry ticket available for all Orkney monuments: Adult £9, Child £2.50, Conc. £7. Admission, shop and refreshments at nearby Tormiston Mill.

RING OF BRODGAR STONE CIRCLE & HENGE

Tel: 0131 668 8600

Stromness, Orkney
Owner: Historic Scotland   **Contact:** The Custodian
A magnificent circle of upright stones with an enclosing ditch spanned by causeways. Of late Neolithic date.
Location: OS Ref. HY294 134. 5m NE of Stromness.
Opening Times: Any reasonable time.
Admission: Free.

Ring of Brodgar Stone Circle & Henge, Orkney.

St Magnus Cathedral, Orkney.

SKARA BRAE & SKAILL HOUSE

SANDWICK, ORKNEY

Owner: *Historic Scotland/Major M R S Macrae*   **Contact:** *The Steward*

Tel: 01856 841815

Skara Brae is one of the best preserved groups of Stone Age houses in Western Europe. Built before the Pyramids, the houses contain stone furniture, hearths and drains. New visitor centre and replica house with joint admission with Skaill House – 17th century home of the Laird who excavated Skara Brae.

Location: OS6 HY231 188. 19m NW of Kirkwall on the B9056.

Opening Times: Apr - Sept: daily, 9.30am - 6.30pm. Oct - Mar: Mon - Sat, 9.30am - 4.30pm, Suns, 2 - 4.30pm.

Admission: Apr - Sept: Adult £4, Child £1.20, Conc. £3. Oct - Mar: Adult £3.20, Child £1, Conc. £2.40. 10% discount for groups (10+). Joint ticket with other Orkney sites available.

[i] Visitor centre. [📷] [♿] Partially suitable. WCs. [🍴] Licensed. [P]
[👥] Free school visits when booked. [🐕] Guide dogs only.

ST MAGNUS CATHEDRAL   Tel: 01856 874894

Broad Street, Kirkwall, Orkney

Owner: Orkney Islands Council   **Contact:** Mr J Rousay

Location: OS Ref. HY449 108. Centre of Kirkwall.

Opening Times: 1 Apr - end Sept: Mon - Sat, 9am - 6pm, Suns, 2 - 6pm. 1 Oct - end Mar: Mon - Sat, 9am - 1pm & 2   5pm.

Admission: Free.

TANKERNESS HOUSE   Tel: 01856 873191 Fax: 01856 874615

Broad Street, Kirkwall, Orkney

Owner: Orkney Islands Council   **Contact:** Bryce S Wilson

A fine vernacular 16th century town house containing museum of Orkney life over 5000 years.

Location: OS Ref. HY446 109. In Kirkwall opposite W end of cathedral.

Opening Times: All year: Mon - Sat, 10.30am - 12.30pm and 1.30 - 5pm, Suns, 2 - 5pm. Apr - Sept: 10.30am - 5pm.

Admission: Adult £2, Conc. Free.

Historic Scotland

Skara Brae, Orkney.

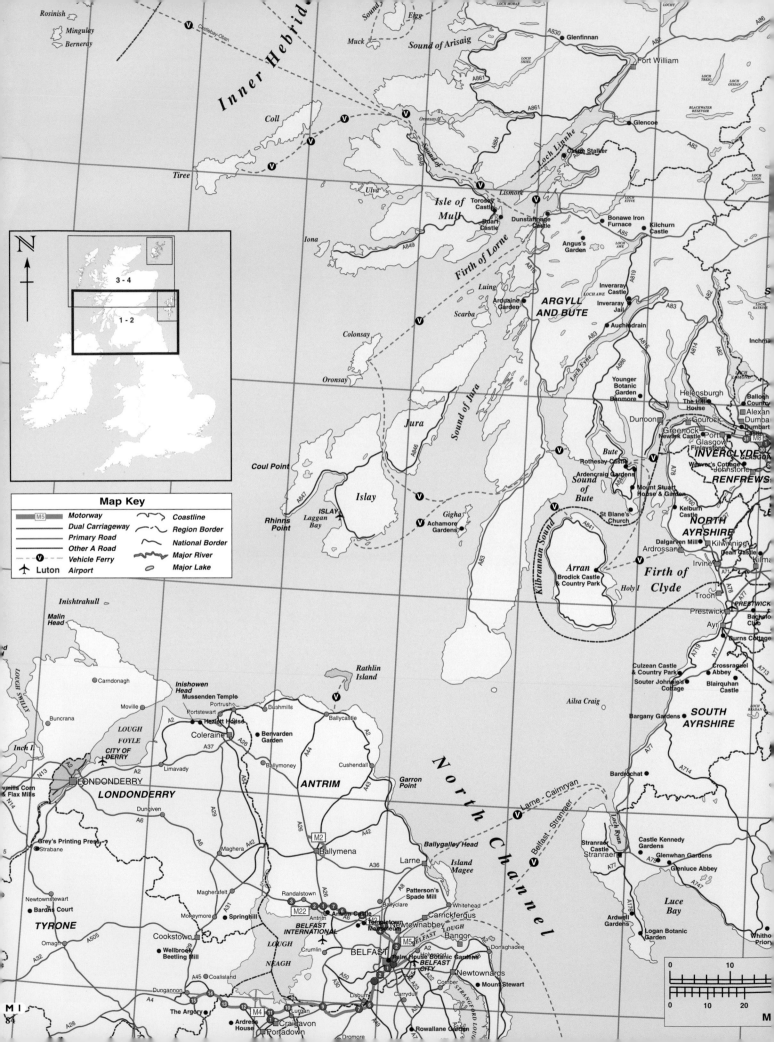

Map Key

M5	Motorway		Coastline
	Dual Carriageway		Region Border
	Primary Road		National Border
	Other A Road		Major River
V	Vehicle Ferry		Major Lake
✈ Luton	Airport		

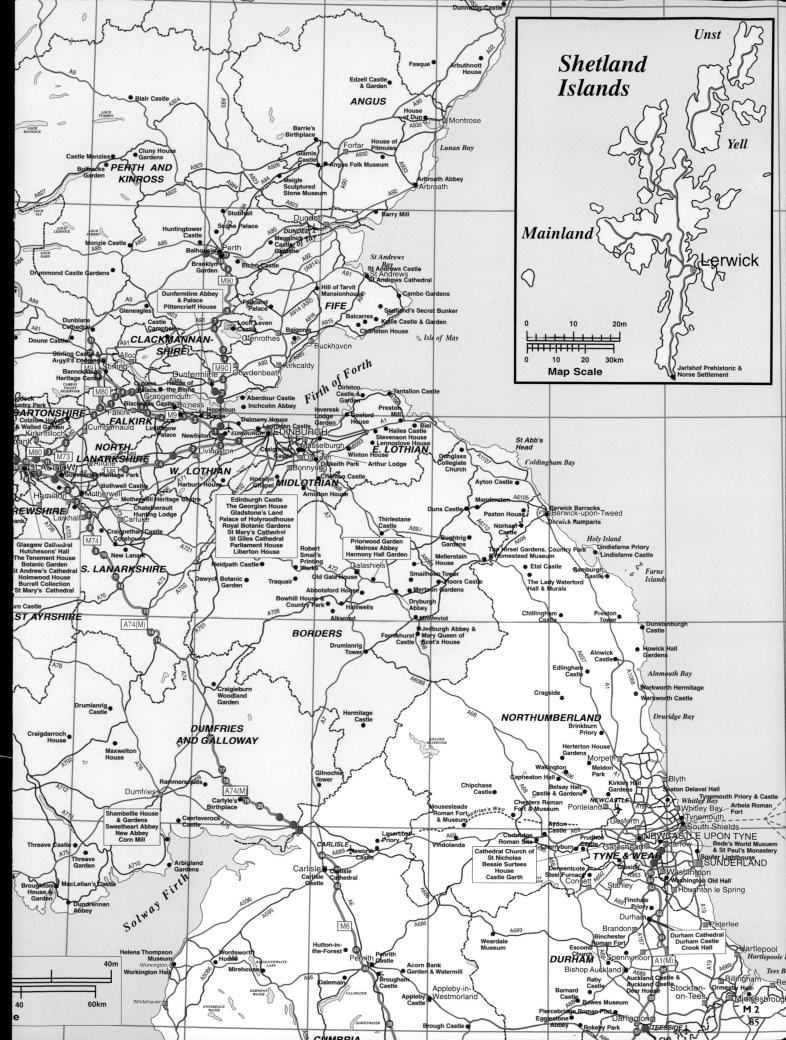

Dunnottar Castle

Shetland Islands

Unst

Yell

Mainland

Lerwick

Jarlshof Prehistoric &
Norse Settlement

0   10   20m

0   10   20   30km

Map Scale

Blair Castle

**PERTH AND
KINROSS**

Castle Menzies
Bolfracks
Garden
Cluny House
Gardens

Drummond Castle Gardens

Monzie Castle

Huntingtower
Castle

Dunblane
Cathedral

Doune Castle

Gleneagles

Castle
Campbell

**CLACKMANNAN-
SHIRE**

Stirling Castle &
Argyll's Lodging
Bannockburn
Heritage Centre

FALKIRK

Alloa
Falkirk
Cumbernauld

**NORTH
LANARKSHIRE**

Summerlee Heritage Park
Airdrie

GLASGOW

Bothwell Castle

Hamilton

Motherwell

Chatelherault
Hunting Lodge
Carluke

Craignethan Castle
Corehouse

New Lanark

S. LANARKSHIRE

Glasgow Cathedral
Hutchesons' Hall
The Tenement House
Botanic Garden
St Andrew's Cathedral
Holmwood House
Burrell Collection
St Mary's Cathedral

RENFREWSHIRE

EAST AYRSHIRE

ANGUS

Fasque
Arbuthnott
House

Edzell Castle
& Garden

House
of Dun
Montrose

Barrie's
Birthplace
Glamis
Castle
Forfar
Angus Folk Museum

Meigle
Sculptured
Stone Museum

Stobhall
Scone Palace

Balhousie
Perth
Branklyn
Garden

Elcho Castle

House of
Pitmuies

Arbroath Abbey
Arbroath

Barry Mill

DUNDEE
Dundee

Megginch
Castle &
Gardens

Dunfermline Abbey
& Palace Pittencrieff House

Loch Leven
Castle

Glenrothes

Dunfermline

Culross
Palace
House of
the Binns
Blackness Castle
Bo'ness

Hopetoun
House

W. LOTHIAN

Linlithgow
Palace

Newliston

Livingston

Harburn House

Falkland
Palace

Hill of Tarvit
Mansionhouse

St Andrews
Bay
St Andrews Castle
St Andrews
St Andrews Cathedral

Cambo Gardens

FIFE

Balcarres

Scotland's Secret Bunker
Kellie Castle & Garden

Charleton House

Kirkcaldy

Cowdenbeath

Balgonie

Buckhaven

Isle of May

Firth of Forth

Aberdour Castle
Inchcolm Abbey

Dirleton
Castle &
Garden
Gosford
House

Preston
Mill

Tantallon Castle

Inveresk
Lodge
Garden

Lauriston Castle
Dalmeny House

EDINBURGH
EDINBURGH

Craigmillar
Castle

Musselburgh

Dalkeith

Hailes Castle
Stevenson House
Lennoxlove House

E. LOTHIAN

Biel

Winton House

Arthur Lodge

*St Abb's
Head*

Coldingham Bay

Dunglass
Collegiate
Church

Dalkeith Park

Bonnyrigg
Chiriton House

Edinburgh Castle
The Georgian House
Gladstone's Land
Palace of Holyroodhouse
Royal Botanic Gardens
St Mary's Cathedral
St Giles Cathedral
Parliament House
Liberton House

MIDLOTHIAN

Rosslyn
Chapel

Arniston House

Robert
Smail's
Printing
Works

Priorwood Garden
Melrose Abbey
Harmony Hall Garden

Ayton Castle

Manderston

Duns Castle
Paxton House

Nornam

Bughtrig
Gardens

Mellerstain
House

The Mirsel Gardens, Country Park
Homestead Museum

Berwick Barracks
Berwick-upon-Tweed
Berwick Ramparts

Holy Island

Lindisfarne Priory
Lindisfarne Castle

*Farne
Islands*

Neidpath Castle

Dawyck Botanic
Garden

Traquair

Abbotsford House

Old Gala House

Galashiels

Thirlestane
Castle

Smailholm Tower
Floors Castle

Mertoun
Gardens

Etal Castle

Bamburgh
Castle

The Lady Waterford
Hall & Murals

Chillingham
Castle

Preston
Tower

Dunstanburgh
Castle

Bowhill House &
Country Park
Halliwells

Dryburgh
Abbey

Monteviot

Jedburgh Abbey &
Mary Queen of
Scot's House

Howick Hall
Gardens

Alnwick
Castle

Alnmouth Bay

Warkworth Hermitage
Warkworth Castle

Druridge Bay

Alkwood

BORDERS

Ferniehurst
Castle

Drumlanrig
Tower

Craigieburn
Woodland
Garden

Drumlanrig
Castle

Craigdarroch
House

Maxwelton
House

**DUMFRIES
AND GALLOWAY**

Rammerscales

Dumfries

Carlyle's
Birthplace

Shambellie House
& Gardens
Sweetheart Abbey
New Abbey
Corn Mill

Caerlaverock
Castle

Arbigland
Gardens

Threave Castle

Broughton
House &
Garden

MacLellan's Castle

Dundrennan
Abbey

Threave
Garden

Solway Firth

Hermitage
Castle

Gilnochie
Tower

*KIELDER
RESERVOIR*

Edlingham
Castle

Cragside

NORTHUMBERLAND

Brinkburn
Priory

Herterton House
Gardens

Wallington

Morpeth

Meldon
Park

Capheaton Hall

Chipchase
Castle

Belsay Hall,
Castle & Gardens

Kirkley Hall
Gardens

Blyth

Seaton Delaval Hall

Tynemouth Priory & Castle
Whitley Bay
Arbeia Roman
Fort

Chesters Roman
Fort & Museum

Ponteland

NEWCASTLE

Gosforth

Housesteads
Roman Fort
& Museum
Hadrian's Wall

Vindolanda

Cathedral Church
of St Nicholas
Bessie Surtees
House
Castle Garth

Corbridge
Roman Site

Aydon
Castle

Cherryburn

Prudhoe
Castle

NEWCASTLE UPON TYNE
Jarrow

Bede's World Musuem
& St Paul's Monastery

Gateshead
South Shields

Derwentcote
Steel Furnace

Consett

Stanley

TYNE & WEAR
Gibside

Washington

SUNDERLAND

Washington Old Hall

Houghton le Spring

Souter Lighthouse

Lanercost
Priory

CARLISLE

Naworth
Castle

Carlisle
Carlisle Castle
Carlisle Cathedral

Finchale
Priory

Brandon

Durham

Peterlee

Escomb

Spennymoor

DURHAM

Durham Cathedral
Durham Castle
Crook Hall

Hartlepool

Hartlepoole

Helena Thompson
Museum
Workington
Workington Hall

Wordsworth
House

Mirehouse

Whitehaven

*BASSENTHWAITE
LAKE*

Hutton-in-
the-Forest

Penrith
Penrith
Castle

Acorn Bank
Garden & Watermill

Dalemain

Brougham
Castle

ULLSWATER

Appleby-in-
Westmorland

Appleby
Castle

Weardale
Museum

Binchester
Roman Fort

Bishop Auckland

Auckland Castle &
Auckland Castle
Deer House

CUMBRIA

*DERWENT
WATER*

*ENNERDALE
WATER*

*DERWENT
WATER*

HAWESWATER

Brough Castle

Barnard
Castle

Raby
Castle

Bowes Museum

Piercebridge Roman Fort

Eggleston
Abbey

Rokeby Park

Darlington

Stockton-
on-Tees

Ormesby Hall

Billingham

Middlesbrough

TEESSIDE

Tees B

Brinkburn
Priory

85

Isle of Lewis

Rudha Rhobhanais
(Butt of Lewis)

Cellar Head

Tolsta Head

Black House

Broad Bay

Tiumpan Head

Lews Castle

STORNOWAY

Chicken Head

Calanais Standing Stones

LOCH ERISORT

Kebock Head

Gt. Bernera

W. LOCH ROAG

Gallan Head

Mealasta I.

LOCH LANGAVAT

LOCH SHELL

Scarp

Hushinish Point

Outer Hebrides

WESTERN ISLES

Taransay

Sound of Taransay

W. LOCH TARBERT

EAST LOCH TARBERT

Scalpay

Shiant Islands

Toe Head

Harris

Shillay

Pabbay

Berneray

Boreray

Vallay

Sound of Harris

Renish Point

Lochmaddy-Tarbert

Tarbert-Uig

The Little Minch

Lochmaddy-Uig

The Minch

Handa Island

Point of Stoer

Rhu Coigach

LOCH ASSYNT

Summer Isles

Stornaway-Ullapool

Greenstone Point

Rudha Reidh

Inverewe Garden

LOCH EWE

FIONN LOCH

LOCH MAREE

Red Point

Rona

LOCH DAMPH

Uibhist a Tuath (North Uist)

Heisker or Monach Islands

BENBECULA

Sound of Monach

Ronay

Beinn na Faoghla (Benbecula)

Wiay

Dunvegan Head

LOCH SNIZORT

Dunvegan Castle

Neist Point

Isle of Skye

LOCH BRACADALE

Sound of Raasay

Raasay

Scalpay

Crowlin Islands

Pabay

LOCH CARRON

Attadale Gardens

LOCH MULLARDOCH

Eilean Donan Castle

LOCH AFFRIC

Uibhist a Deas (South Uist)

Rudha Hallagro

Soay

Inner Sound

Sound of Sleat

Clan Donald Visitor Centre & Armadale Garden

LOCH HOURN

LOCH CLUANIE

A87

Sound of Barra

Eriskay

BARRA

Greian Head

Barra

A888

Vatersay

Kisimul Castle

Sandray

Castlebay-Oban

Rosinish

Mingulay

Berneray

Canna

Sound of Canna

Cuillin Sound

Rum

Sound of Rum

Eigg

Muck

Sound of Arisaig

Glenfinnan

LOCH SHIEL

Fort William

Inner Hebrides

Coll

Oransay

Glencoe

Loch Linnhe

Tiree

Castle Stalker

Ulva

Lismore

Isle of Mull

Torosay Castle

Duart Castle

Dunstaffnage Castle

Angus's Garden

Bonawe Iron Furnace

Kilchurn Castle

LOCH AWE

Iona

A849

Firth of Lorne

Luing

Inveraray Castle

Ardmaddy Garden

Scarba

Inverarary Jail

ARGYLL AND BUTE

Map Scale

0   10   20   40m

0   10   20   40   60km

N

3 - 4

1 - 2

Orkney Islands

Mainland

Hoy

Kirkwall

Carrick House

Broch of Gurness

Skaill House

Skara Brae

Balfour Castle

Ring of Brodgar Stone Circles & Henge

Maes Howe

Tankerness House
Bishop's Palace
Earl's Palace
St Magnus' Cathedral

Scotland

Pentland Firth

Island of Stroma

Dunnet Head

Duncansby Head

Whiten Head

Strathy Point

Noss Head

WICK

LOCH HOPE
LOCH AN DHERRIE
LOCH CRAGGIE
LOCH MEADIE
LOCH LOYAL
LOCH NAVER
LOCH RIMSDALE
LOCH NAN CLAR
LOCH BADANLOCH
LOCH AN RUATHAIR
LOCH FIAG
LOCH FLAG
LOCH SHIN
LOCH CALDER
LOCH SHURRERY
LOCH MORE

A836
A897
A882
A9
(A895)

Dunrobin Castle

A839
A940
A836
A9

Dornock Firth

Moray Firth

LOCH SHIN
LOCH MORIE
LOCH GLASS

Hugh Miller's Cottage
Cromarty Courthouse

Fort George

Brodie Castle

Dallas Dhu Distillery

Spynie Palace

Elgin

Elgin Cathedral

Pluscarden Abbey

Fraserburgh

Duff House

MORAY

Craigston Castle

Delgatie Castle

Peterhead

INVERNESS

Inverness

Cawdor Castle

Culloden

Drummuir Castle

Balvenie Castle

Huntly Castle

Fyvie Castle

Haddo House

Dochfour Gardens

LOCH DUNTELCHAIG

Urquhart Castle

LOCH NESS

LOCH MHOR

Ballindalloch Castle

Leith Hall

Tolquhon Castle

Pitmedden Garden

Doune of Rothiemurcus

Corgarff Castle

Kildrummy Castle
Kildrummy Castle Garden

Candacraig Garden & Gallery

ABERDEENSHIRE

Monymusk Walled Garden

ABERDEEN

Castle Fraser & Garden

Crathes Castle

Drum Castle

ABERDEEN CITY

Aberdeen

To Stromness
To Lerwick

St Machar's Cathedral
Transepts
Cruickshank Botanic Garden
Provost Skene's House
Duthie Park & Winter Gardens

Braemar Castle

Balmoral Castle

LOCH LAGGAN
LOCH ERICHT

Dunnottar Castle

Fasque

Arbuthnott House

Edzell Castle & Garden

Blair Castle

LOCH TUMMEL
LOCH RANNOCH

ANGUS

House of Dun

Montrose

Barrie's Birthplace

Cluny House Gardens

Castle Menzies

Bolfracks Garden

Forfar

Houe of Pitmuies

Lunan Bay

Glamis Castle

Angus Folk Museum

PERTH AND KINROSS

LOCH LYON
LOCH VOILE

Monzie Castle

Huntingtower Castle

Scone Palace

Perth

Meigle Sculptured Stone Museum

Stobhall

Barry Mill

Arbroath Abbey

Dundee

DUNDEE

Firth of Tay

Drummond Castle Gardens

Branklyn Garden

Elcho Castle

Megginch Castle Gardens

St Andrews Bay

St Andrews Castle

STIRLING

LOCH KATRINE

Dunblane Cathedral

Gleneagles

Falkland Palace

Hill of Tarvit Mansionhouse

FIFE

St Andrews Cathedral

Cambo Gardens

Scotland's Secret Bunker

Kellie Castle & Garden

Index of all Properties

A

Abbotsford House, Borders 15
Aberdour Castle, Perthshire/Fife 53
Achamore Gardens, West Highlands/Stirling 62
Aikwood Tower & James Hogg Exhibition, Borders 15
Angus Folk Museum, Perthshire/Fife 53
Angus's Garden, West Highlands/Stirling 62
Arbigland Gardens, SW Scotland 26
Arbroath Abbey, Perthshire/Fife 53
Arbuthnott House, Grampian 69
Ardencraig Gardens, West Highlands/Stirling 62
Arduaine Garden, West Highlands/Stirling 62
Ardwell Gardens, SW Scotland 26
Argyll's Lodging, West Highlands/Stirling 60
Arniston House, Edinburgh City, Coast & Countryside 35
Arthur Lodge, Edinburgh City, Coast & Countryside 35
Attadale Gardens, The Highlands & Skye 78
Auchindrain Township, West Highlands/ Stirling 62
Ayton Castle, Borders 15

B

Bachelors' Club, SW Scotland 26
Balfluig Castle, Grampian 69
Balfour Castle, Outer Islands 82
Balgonie Castle, Perthshire/Fife 53
Balhousie Castle (Black Watch Museum), Perthshire/Fife 53
Ballindalloch Castle, The Highlands & Skye 78
Balloch Castle Country Park, West Highlands/Stirling 62
Balmoral Castle, Grampian 69
Balvenie Castle, Grampian 69
Bannockburn Heritage Centre, West Highlands/Stirling 62
Bardrochat, SW Scotland 26
Bargany Gardens, SW Scotland 26
Barrie's Birthplace, Perthshire/Fife 53
Barry Mill, Perthshire/Fife 53
Biel, Edinburgh City, Coast & Countryside 35
Bishop's & Earl's Palaces, Outer Islands 82
Black House, Outer Islands 82
Blackness Castle, Edinburgh City, Coast & Countryside 35
Blair Castle, Perthshire/Fife 50
Blairquhan Castle, SW Scotland 24
Bolfracks Garden, Perthshire/Fife 53
Bonawe Iron Furnace, West Highlands/Stirling ...62
Botanic Gardens, Greater Glasgow & Clyde Valley 45
Bothwell Castle, Greater Glasgow & Clyde Valley 45
Bowhill House & Country Park, Borders 12
Braemar Castle, Grampian 69
Branklyn Garden, Perthshire/Fife 53
Broch of Gurness, Outer Islands 82
Brodick Castle & Country Park, SW Scotland 27
Brodie Castle, Grampian 69
Broughton House & Garden, SW Scotland 27
Bughtrig Garden, Borders 15
Burns' Cottage, South West Scotland 27
Burrell Collection, Greater Glasgow & Clyde Valley 45

C

Caerlaverock Castle, SW Scotland 27
Calanais Standing Stones, Outer Islands 82
Cambo Gardens, Perthshire/Fife 53
Candacraig Garden & Gallery, Grampian 70
Cardoness Castle, SW Scotland 27
Carlyle's Birthplace, SW Scotland 27
Carrick House, Outer Islands 82
Castle Campbell, West Highlands/Stirling 62
Castle Fraser & Garden, Grampian 70
Castle Kennedy Gardens, SW Scotland 28
Castle Menzies, Perthshire/Fife 53
Castle Stalker, West Highlands/Stirling 62
Cawdor Castle, The Highlands & Skye 76
Charleton House, Perthshire/Fife 54
Chatelherault Hunting Lodge, Greater Glasgow & Clyde Valley 45
Clan Donald Visitor Centre & Armadale Castle Garden, The Highlands & Skye 78
Cluny House Gardens, Perthshire/Fife 54
Colzium House & Walled Garden, Greater Glasgow & Clyde Valley 45
Corehouse, Greater Glasgow & Clyde Valley 45
Corgarff Castle, Grampian 70
Craigdarroch House, SW Scotland 28
Craigieburn Garden, SW Scotland 28

Craigmillar Castle, Edinburgh City, Coast & Countryside 35
Craignethan Castle, Greater Glasgow & Clyde Valley 45
Craigston Castle, Grampian 70
Crathes Castle, Grampian 70
Crichton Castle, Edinburgh City, Coast & Countryside 35
Cromarty Courthouse, The Highlands & Skye 78
Crossraguel Abbey, SW Scotland 28
Cruickshank Botanic Garden, Grampian 70
Culloden, The Highlands & Skye 78
Culross Palace, Perthshire/Fife 54
Culzean Castle & Country Park, SW Scotland 28

D

Dalgarven Mill, SW Scotland 28
Dalkeith Country Park, Edinburgh City, Coast & Countryside 35
Dallas Dhu Distillery, Grampian 70
Dalmeny House, Edinburgh City, Coast & Countryside 32
Dawyck Botanic Garden, Borders 15
Dean Castle Country Park, SW Scotland 28
Delgatie Castle, Grampian 71
Dirleton Castle & Garden, Edinburgh City, Coast & Countryside 35
Dochfour Gardens, The Highlands & Skye 78
Doune Castle, West Highlands/Stirling 63
Doune of Rothiemurchus, The, The Highlands & Skye 79
Drum Castle, Grampian 71
Drumlanrig Castle, SW Scotland 25
Drumlanrig's Tower, Borders 16
Drummond Castle Gardens, Perthshire/Fife 54
Drummuir Castle, Grampian 71
Dryburgh Abbey, Borders 16
Duart Castle, West Highlands/Stirling 63
Duff House, Grampian 68
Dumbarton Castle, West Highlands/Stirling 63
Dunblane Cathedral, West Highlands/Stirling 63
Dundrennan Abbey, SW Scotland 28
Dunfermline Abbey & Palace, Perthshire/Fife 54
Dunglass Collegiate Church, Edinburgh City, Coast & Countryside 36
Dunnottar Castle, Grampian 71
Dunrobin Castle, The Highlands & Skye 78
Duns Castle, Borders 16
Dunstaffnage Castle, West Highlands/Stirling 63
Dunvegan Castle, The Highlands & Skye 77
Duthie Park & Winter Gardens, Grampian 71

E

Edinburgh Castle, Edinburgh City, Coast & Countryside 36
Edzell Castle & Garden, Perthshire/Fife............54
Eilean Donan Castle, The Highlands & Skye........79
Elcho Castle, Perthshire/Fife 54
Elgin Cathedral, Grampian 71

F

Falkland Palace, Perthshire/Fife............55
Fasque, Grampian 71
Ferniehirst Castle, Borders............16
Finlaystone, Greater Glasgow & Clyde Valley 45
Floors Castle, Borders............13
Fort George, The Highlands & Skye 79
Fyvie Castle, Grampian............72

G

Galloway House Gardens, SW Scotland 28
Georgian House, The, Edinburgh City, Coast & Countryside 36
Gilnockie's Tower, SW Scotland............28
Gladstone's Land, Edinburgh City, Coast & Countryside 36
Glamis Castle, Perthshire/Fife 51
Glasgow Cathedral, Greater Glasgow & Clyde Valley 45
Glencoe, West Highlands/Stirling 63
Gleneagles, Perthshire/Fife 55
Glenfinnan, The Highlands & Skye 79
Glenluce Abbey, SW Scotland 28
Glenwhan Gardens, SW Scotland 28
Gosford House, Edinburgh City, Coast & Countryside 37
Greenbank, Greater Glasgow & Clyde Valley 45

H

Haddo House, Grampian 72

Hailes Castle, Edinburgh City, Coast & Countryside 37
Halliwell's House Museum, Borders 17
Harburn House, Edinburgh City, Coast & Countryside 33
Harmony Garden, Borders 17
Hermitage Castle, Borders 17
Hill House, The, West Highlands/Stirling 64
Hill of Tarvit Mansionhouse, Perthshire/Fife 55
Hirsel Gardens, Country Park & Homestead Museum, The, Borders 17
Holmwood House, Greater Glasgow & Clyde Valley 46
Hopetoun House, Edinburgh City, Coast & Countryside 34
House of Dun, Perthshire/Fife 55
House of Pitmuies, Perthshire/Fife 55
House of The Binns, Edinburgh City, Coast & Countryside 37
Huntingtower Castle, Perthshire/Fife 55
Huntly Castle, Grampian 72
Hutchesons' Hall, Greater Glasgow & Clyde Valley 46

I

Inchcolm Abbey, Perthshire/Fife 55
Inchmahome Priory, Perthshire/Fife 56
Inveraray Castle, West Highlands/Stirling 61
Inveraray Jail, West Highlands/Stirling 64
Inveresk Lodge Garden, Edinburgh City, Coast & Countryside 37
Inverewe Garden, The Highlands & Skye 79

J

Jarlshof Prehistoric & Norse Settlement, Outer Islands 82
Jedburgh Abbey, Borders 17

K

Kelburn, Greater Glasgow & Clyde Valley 44
Kellie Castle & Garden, Perthshire/Fife 56
Kiessimul Castle, Outer Islands 82
Kilchurn Castle, West Highlands/Stirling 64
Kildrummy Castle, Grampian 72
Kildrummy Castle Garden, Grampian 72

L

Lauriston Castle, Edinburgh City, Coast & Countryside 37
Leith Hall, Grampian 72
Lennoxlove House, Edinburgh City, Coast & Countryside 37
Liberton House, Edinburgh 37
Linlithgow Palace, Edinburgh City, Coast & Countryside 38
Loch Leven Castle, Perthshire/Fife 56
Logan Botanic Garden, SW Scotland 29

M

MacLellan's Castle, SW Scotland 29
Maes Howe, Outer Islands 82
Manderston, Borders 14
Mary Queen of Scots' House, Borders 17
Maxwelton House, SW Scotland 29
Megginch Castle Gardens, Perthshire/Fife 56
Meigle Sculptured Stone Museum, Perthshire/Fife 56
Mellerstain House, Borders 18
Melrose Abbey, Borders 18
Mertoun Gardens, Borders 18
Miller's Cottage, Hugh, The Highlands & Skye 79
Monteviot House Garden, Borders 18
Monymusk Walled Garden, Grampian 72
Monzie Castle, Perthshire/Fife 56
Motherwell Heritage Centre, Greater Glasgow & Clyde Valley 46
Mount Stuart House & Garden, West Highlands/Stirling 64
Mugdock Country Park, Greater Glasgow & Clyde Valley 46

N

Neidpath Castle, Borders 18
New Abbey Corn Mill, SW Scotland 29
New Lanark, Greater Glasgow & Clyde Valley 46
Newark Castle, Greater Glasgow & Clyde Valley 46
Newliston, Edinburgh City, Coast & Countryside 38

O

Old Gala House, Borders 18

P

Palace of Holyroodhouse, Edinburgh City, Coast & Countryside 38
Parliament House, Edinburgh City, Coast & Countryside 40
Paxton House, Borders 20
Pitmedden Garden, Grampian 73
Pittencrieff House, Perthshire/Fife 56
Pluscarden Abbey, Grampian 73
Pollok House, Greater Glasgow & Clyde Valley ...47
Preston Mill, Edinburgh City, Coast & Countryside 40
Priorwood Garden & Dried Flower Shop, Borders 20
Provost Skene's House, Grampian 73

R

Rammerscales, SW Scotland 29
Ring of Brodgar Stone Circle & Henge, Outer Islands 82
Rosslyn Chapel, Edinburgh City, Coast & Countryside 40
Rothesay Castle, West Highlands/Stirling 64
Royal Botanic Garden, Edinburgh City, Coast & Countryside 40

S

St Andrews Castle, Perthshire/Fife 57
St Andrews Cathedral, Perthshire/Fife 57
St Blane's Church, West Highlands/Stirling 64
St Giles' Cathedral, Edinburgh City, Coast & Countryside 40
St Machar's Cathedral Transepts, Grampian 73
St Magnus Cathedral, Outer Islands 83
St Mary's Cathedral, Edinburgh City, Coast & Countryside 40
St Mary's Cathedral, Greater Glasgow & Clyde Valley 47
Scone Palace, Perthshire/Fife 52
Scotland's Secret Bunker, Perthshire/Fife 57
Scottish National Portrait Gallery, Edinburgh City, Coast & Countryside 40
Shambellie House & Gardens, SW Scotland 29
Skara Brae & Skaill House, Outer Islands 83
Smail's Printing Works, Robert, Borders 20
Smailholm Tower, Borders 20
Sorn Castle, SW Scotland 29
Souter Johnnie's Cottage, SW Scotland 29
Spynie Palace, Grampian 73
Stevenson House, Edinburgh City, Coast & Countryside 40
Stirling Castle, West Highlands/Stirling 64
Stobhall Gardens & Chapel, Perthshire/Fife 57
Stranraer Castle, SW Scotland 29
Summerlee Heritage Park, Greater Glasgow & Clyde Valley 47
Sweetheart Abbey, SW Scotland 29

T

Tankerness House, Outer Islands 83
Tantallon Castle, Edinburgh City, Coast & Countryside 41
Tenement House, The, Greater Glasgow & Clyde Valley 47
Thirlestane Castle, Borders 20
Threave Castle, SW Scotland 29
Threave Garden, SW Scotland 29
Tolquhon Castle, Grampian 73
Torosay Castle & Gardens, West Highlands/ Stirling 65
Traquair, Borders 21

U

Urquhart Castle, The Highlands & Skye 79

W

Weaver's Cottage, Greater Glasgow & Clyde Valley 47
Whithorn Priory, SW Scotland 29
Winton House, Edinburgh, Coast & Countryside 41

Y

Younger Botanic Garden Benmore, West Highlands/Stirling 65